From Extendicare Brampton

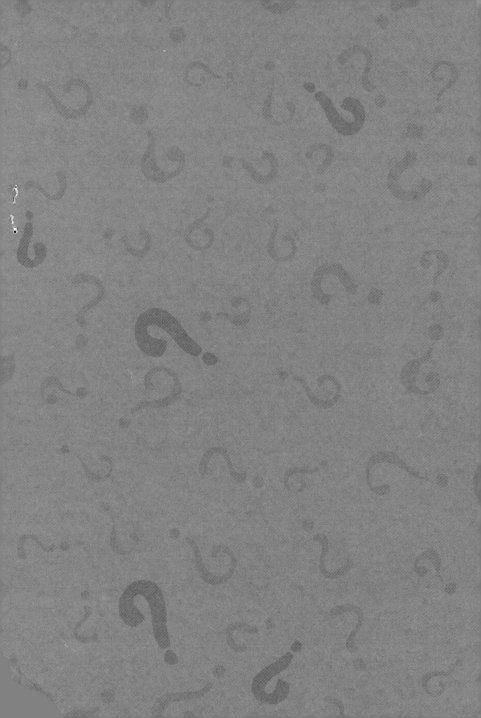

NOW WHAT?

Managing the Emotional Journey
of Long Term Care For Families

By
Deborah Bakti

NOW WHAT?

Managing the Emotional Journey of Long Term Care for Families

by Deborah Bakti

FOR PERMISSIONS CONTACT:

Deborah Bakti
deborah@deborahbakti.com

COVER DESIGN: Cleo Lant, WHYDEA Inc.

BOOK DESIGN: Peter Pereira, WHYDEA Inc.

AUTHOR PHOTO: Nat Caron Photography

ISBN: 978-1-9991621-2-2

To all the wonderful people who work, live and visit in long term care.

CONTENTS

FOREWORD BY BARBARA TARRANT

I have been a caregiver for my husband Patrick since 2011, when he was diagnosed with Alzheimer Disease. I've spent four-and-a-half years as his primary caregiver and five years as his co-caregiver. He became a resident of a long term care home in November 2015. The day of his admission was the hardest day of my life!

When Patrick and I first received the diagnosis, it didn't come as a surprise to us. He was the third in his family to be diagnosed. But we didn't think we knew everything about the disease, so we reached out to the Alzheimer's Society of Canada for advice and support. Our thinking was if we learned as much as we could about the stages of the disease—there are seven stages—we would be able to cope better.

We learned that no two people with Alzheimer's progress through the different stages at the same rate. So, when my husband exhibited a dramatic change in behaviour with delusional thoughts, I had no idea what was happening. Nor did I know the effects that severe emotional stress can have on our body. This was something I learned after experiencing a small stroke! Fortunately, I fully recovered, but it was a wakeup call.

I think all primary caregivers know that the day will come when they can no longer continue to provide the care their loved one requires. Safety becomes a major issue. But when the day comes and you move your loved one into a long term care home, nothing prepares you for the multitude of emotions you will experience. Your head tells you this is the right decision, but your heart is breaking! Looking back, that admission day was a blur. I remember meeting many people and doing lots of paperwork, but it was just too much to take in. But one memory stands out. I cried all the way home! They were tears of guilt along with relief. Upon arriving home and walking into familiar surroundings, I truly felt alone.

Your journey within the long term care system begins. You are a novice, with a "million questions and worries." I know the staff in my husband's home did their best to make those first weeks as friendly and encouraging as possible. But now, on reflection, I learned "by the seat of my pants!"

How I wish I had this book you are now reading. I met Deborah in 2019. She conducted several family focus groups in my husband's LTC home. By this time, I had become a pro, or so I thought! But

I wanted to participate in these groups because I thought I could contribute to help new families.

I soon learned that those "million questions and worries" I had in the beginning could have been less traumatic if I had Deborah's own experiences, both personal and professional to rely on. Every chapter of this book you're now reading brought back memories, especially emotional ones. But today, I am stronger and better prepared for the final stages of my husband's life. He stills knows who I am, after 39 years of marriage. When I visit, he still asks me to marry him! He is serious! God bless him.

Deborah's book is a treasure for all new families beginning their long term care journey. As she says it is not an easy one and we sure didn't ask for it! I can think of many "journeys" I would have chosen instead. But as a new long term care resident's family member your role now is that of co-caregiver. I found it hard to give up my role as primary caregiver. You know you have to trust the new primary caregivers; it is best for your loved one and yourself. "Trust" becomes a very important emotion.

Deborah offers in her book, not only her professional experience in the LTC field, but her personal one as well. She has been on this journey with three of her own loved ones. She wants to bring you some reassurance, comfort and some real perspectives that can support you. Her book is a much-needed guide for families new to the long term care experience.

Look to your own strength and resilience, which will be tested, as you begin this journey. You know in your heart that it is the best decision for your loved one. Reach out for support. Deborah's book will offer that support and guidance.

Best wishes,

Barbara Tarrant
2020

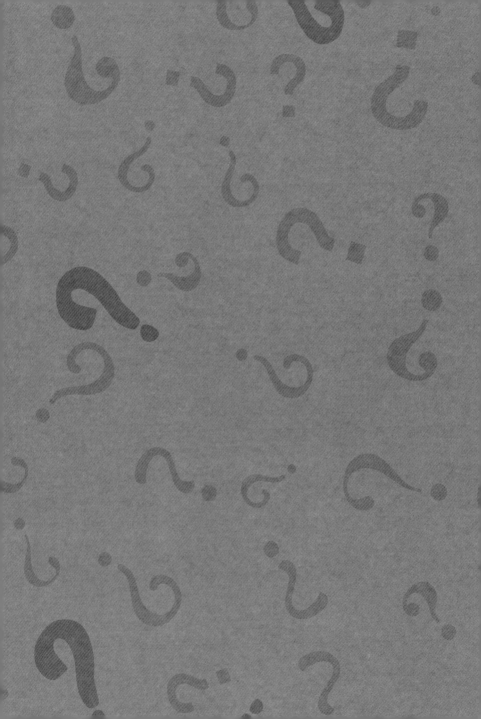

INTRODUCTION

"When I get old and can't take care of myself, I want to live in a nursing home with a bunch of people I don't know." – Said no one. Ever.

Let's face it, the idea of "ending up" in a nursing home ourselves can influence how we feel about moving a loved one into long term care. It's not usually the option we run to – instead, it typically becomes the only viable option.

Long term care (LTC) is a key part of our health care system; it's a much-needed service. But it's not always a solution we want for our loved ones.

You may be asking yourself, "Now what?" Wherever you are on your journey - whether that's considering LTC, or you've already made the decision and are waiting for availability, or you've already joined the "Resident's Family Member Club"- this book is for you.

Although the prime focus of this book is long term care, if you have a loved one in Retirement, Assisted Living or Memory Care, you will also find much of the information and resources in this book helpful. After all, you are also a resident's family member.

Think of this as a playbook of sorts: It's not so much about *"How does the system work?"* but more *"How do I make this work for me and my family?"* This book will help prepare and equip you with the knowledge and tools you need to navigate through the various stages, including acceptance and appreciation. All without wearing yourself out physically and emotionally.

I understand what you're going through. I've been there myself.

I first became a resident's family member when my dad was admitted into LTC in early 2011, followed by my husband three months later. Then my mom moved into Retirement, then Assisted Living several years after that. Ironically, I was also working in seniors' care as a Vice President with a company that operated over 100 long term care homes in Canada. I had inside knowledge of how things worked in the LTC system and thought I had the upper hand.

During this time, I had my own hands full working full-time and raising two kids. At 62 years of age my husband Ty was diagnosed with an extremely rare disease called Erdheim-Chester disease (ECD). It was so rare in fact, that it took 18 months for doctors to identify his illness. At the time, only 400 people in the world had also been diagnosed with ECD.

We were also told that Erdheim-Chester was degenerative, incurable, and fatal. At this point, because of the decline in Ty's health and abilities, he was receiving home care twice a day, five days a week, in addition to attending an adult day care centre two to three times a week.

Ty was then admitted into LTC just a few months after my dad in April 2011. For many months following, I oscillated between visiting my dad in his home on one side of the city, and my husband in another on the other side of the city. It was emotionally draining and incredibly surreal, to say the least.

Perhaps you've already been through the wringer in coming to terms with your loved one's health changes and the degree that they now require the care and support of an LTC home. You may also be feeling conflicting emotions – sadness, frustration, guilt, anger, worry – now that a team of caregivers are taking care of them. You may also feel some guilt about feeling relieved.

Or maybe you are wondering if, or when, it

will be time to consider LTC for your loved one. Perhaps you're watching your parents continue to live in their home, but are struggling with their daily activities. Or they're having memory issues and you worry about their safety and well being. You are not alone.

In Canada, almost 400 families go through this life-changing experience every single day, as a loved one is admitted into LTC. That's close to 7,500 families every single month who walk through the doors of an LTC home feeling a myriad of emotions.

This is a huge life change for you and your family. If you have never stepped foot in a home before now, it can feel like a scary transition.

This is a new arrangement, one that requires new relationships. You'll be meeting many care team members on different shifts who are all responsible for taking care of your loved one, who is now their new resident. You'll visit the home to spend time with your loved one, where you'll meet other residents and their family members.

Making this new reality work isn't always easy. Integrating this into your life can be challenging.

That's why I wrote this book. This is the book I

wish I had when I became a family member. I want to help ease some of the emotional distress you may be feeling.

We hear negative stories in the media about LTC. Perhaps you've also heard stories from other people about their own experiences. Maybe your loved one made you promise to never send them to an "old folks' home," only you are now unable to keep up with the growing demands of their care. Or they've been living in a retirement home, but now need additional help and care. Others may be referred to LTC after a lengthy hospital stay.

Whatever path you're on, it's challenging to accept this new reality, or to even know what to do next. You may be asking yourself, "Now what... will their lives be like? Now what...will MY life be like?"

Some of you may feel moving to an institutional setting isn't the ideal place you imagined for your loved one. For others, it may be your only choice. The impact on family members doesn't typically get discussed. The focus tends to be on the resident. After all this is a big life change for them. And yet, families are profoundly affected too.

In this book, I'll share my own admission day experience and shed some light on your new identity as a resident's family member. You'll also learn about the emotional journey through the Seven A's – from awareness to appreciation. There is a chapter written by Edy Nathan, who is a licenced therapist and author of *It's Grief: The Dance of Self-Discovery Through Trauma and Loss.* Edy shares her insights on how to "dance with the grief." I provide perspective from another vantage point of your admission day experience – the people who work in long term care. You'll also read about some common misconceptions that other families have shared. My hope is they will help increase your knowledge, clarify expectations, and minimize disappointment. I've also written a chapter on the three different types of "family flavours" to help you reflect on what your family flavour may be.

Being a practical person, I wanted to provide useful tips and tools that will assist you with the changes in your life, so you're able to create the best possible relationships with the care team members. After all, they are the ones who are now largely responsible for providing quality care, compassion, and support to your loved one.

You will find this book helpful if you're feeling:

- Worried that your loved one is going to dislike living in long term care, or is upset with you because of it

- Judged by friends and family who ask why you couldn't keep your loved one at home

- Wishful that it didn't have to come to this point

- Grief and guilt for making this decision

- Worried about how the people working in the home are going to take care of your loved one

- Concerned the care providers don't know you, your family, or your loved one

My motivation for writing this book is to help you along the journey you're now on. When I became a family member I was working in seniors' care. That should have given me an advantage, yet I still struggled with the emotional roller coaster and physical impact it had on me as a spouse, a mother, and daughter. It was through this very personal journey, with operational insight, that I created the framework we'll explore in this book.

It's normal to feel some resistance, even resentment, about this new reality. You likely have questions or may not even know what you don't know. If your concerns are keeping you up at night or if you're questioning your decision to place your loved one into LTC, then this book can help.

At the time of writing **Now What?**, the world was hit by the COVID-19 pandemic, and care homes were severely impacted by this virus. As we lived through lock downs, and phases of re-opening, and closing, the residents living in LTC were the most vulnerable. Families have also been impacted with restricted visitations and heartbreaking loss.

Whether you're admitting a loved one during a pandemic, a flu outbreak, or during less turbulent times, it's still an incredibly personal and emotional journey.

This book does not address the political or funding issues associated with LTC. Nor am I addressing other business issues related to clinical delivery of care or staffing levels. There are other resources you can access for that lens.

I know that most people who work in seniors' care are incredibly compassionate, empathetic, and caring human beings. They didn't get into this work for the money, that's for sure! They love caring for seniors and being a helpful companion and support to them and their families.

I have lived and worked within Seniors' Care – both as a corporate leader and as a family member. I am passionate about creating and sharing resources that educate, equip, and inspire the professional caregivers and families to develop empathy and connection with each other. When there is understanding, trust, and respect, then a powerful partnership in care can happen.

This book is for and about you. Your experience. Your emotions. Your ability to journey through the Seven A's and manage this experience as a resident's family member as best you can. I want this book to help expand your ability and your resilience throughout this emotional journey.

As the title suggests, it IS a journey. How you perceive, experience, and relate to yourself and others may change – from that first admission day to the final day. I hope this is a book you can come back to, re-read sections, and gleam something helpful or meaningful as you continue in your journey.

Viktor Frankl, author of *Man's Search for Meaning* said:

> ***"When we are no longer able to change a situation, we are challenged to change ourselves."***

With insight, encouragement, and the right tools, you can take the lead in influencing what you can – which is you!

CHAPTER 1

My Admission Day Experience

I n March 2011, three years after his symptoms of Erdheim-Chester started, my husband Ty was admitted into long term care. I still remember how that day felt – how intense and almost unbearable the anxiety was.

The night before, I crawled into bed feeling sick to my stomach. The reality that our lives, including those of our two teenage children, were about to dramatically change was sinking in. Ty was going to spend the rest of his shortened life living in an LTC home and I couldn't do anything to change this.

I lay awake trying to imagine what our new lives were going to look like. I knew Ty would be moving into a semi-private room with a man he hadn't met before. A man who would now be his roommate. That they'd only be separated by a curtain. That my husband would not even be able to lock his own bedroom door. I also knew Ty would get to the point where he'd need others to help bathe, dress, and feed him each day.

This was all happening to the man that I'd been married to for 25 years. A man who was once strong, independent, still charming, and quite the troublemaker! He was slowly experiencing what seemed like death by a thousand cuts. His cognitive functioning was already impaired and continuing to worsen. It was hard for him to speak clearly, as the disease caused his speech to be slurred. His mobility had deteriorated and every day that passed was going to be his best day. He was losing his independence, his physical, mental, and emotional capacities, and I could see the frustration and fear on his face.

The logical side of my brain said, "This is the best and only reasonable solution. It's the only way." And that's what my case manager, friends, family and colleagues at work also told me. But I could feel myself resisting our sad new reality, not quite believing this was actually happening. I felt the conflict by feelings of guilt, sadness, and hoping this truly was the best decision and right step for all of us.

The next morning, as I helped Ty out of our car into his wheelchair and pushed him to the front doors of the home, I felt myself become unhinged. In that moment, I was acutely aware of what I was doing. I was taking my husband to this place where he was going to live – until he died.

We found the reception area, introduced ourselves, and were directed to a family visiting room. All the while, the overwhelming feelings of grief and guilt competed for my attention. The two of us sat in this room and waited for a meeting we needed but didn't want.

In my professional capacity, I had been in a lot of LTC homes as part of my work. However, this wasn't that kind of visit. This was personal. Deeply personal. It was in this moment I suddenly realized I was now a resident's wife.

While waiting, I tried to distract myself by looking around and taking in the activities. I looked out the window to where the nursing station was. I watched other residents wheel and walk by. I inhaled the sharp scent of floor cleaner. I heard the call bell ring as I tried to swallow the lump in my throat that was holding back tears.

I tried making small talk with Ty in an effort to cut the tension, but it felt awkward. I suspect if he wasn't reliant on a wheelchair, my husband would have bolted out of the waiting room! This is not how he envisioned his life either. He thought he was going to live a long and healthy life into his nineties, like his grandfather. Throughout his illness, Ty truly believed he was going to get better and be able to come back home to live with his family.

Finally, after twenty agonizing minutes, the door opened and the care team walked in. There were three or four of them, led by the Director of Care who introduced herself to us. The others also extended their hands and said their name and department. My head was so full, I could barely take in their names or their roles. One of them smiled and somewhat out of breath said, "I'm so sorry we're late. You know, there's always something going on around here!"

I didn't even know what to say to that. I thought, "Really? Wow, that's too bad. Because you know what? There's something going on for us too!" Instead, I said nothing. And I waited for what came next, feeling somewhat annoyed and disrespected. Not a great way to start the relationship.

The Director of Care kicked off our admission meeting and shuffled paperwork on her lap. Then the questioning started: "Let's review, what medications is he taking?" "Does he prefer a bath or a shower?" The questioning continued. She wanted to know everything about Ty's personal care, toileting, financials, emergency contacts. It went on and on.

I felt uncomfortable answering questions with Ty sitting right there, also trying to process everything. I wondered if it was too much to expect the staff to understand how awful this felt for us right now.

Then, the really awkward question was asked: "If something happens, do you want us to resuscitate him?"

Intellectually, I knew these questions were required by the Ministry of Health, which provides funding to the home. I worked in the system; I knew the requirements. I just couldn't believe they would be asking that question of me now.

As I straddled my professional knowledge with my reeling emotions, any and all rational thoughts evaporated. At that moment, I became a 49-year-old-wife of a 63-year-old man who had to move into LTC because his body and brain had betrayed him.

It took every ounce of focus and determination to hold myself together in front of Ty and these strangers. I wasn't okay. It was when I returned home, the home I no longer shared with my husband, that I completely broke down.

....

My experience with Ty's admission to LTC sparked my decision to switch gears in my career. I realized my personal experience as a family member and my knowledge of the industry were valuable not only to people who worked in seniors' care, but also to the families of new residents. I left my corporate job and started a consulting business for seniors' care organizations. I created a framework called "RECIPE for Transforming Families into Fans" and delivered keynotes and workshops for staff. Then I wrote RECIPE for Empathy; Six Strategies to Transform your Families into Fans, which was published in 2019.

The following passage is from that first book:

It was a few months after Ty had passed away and as our conversation meandered through how I was "dealing" with his passing, she asked about our admission day experience. I reflected on that most difficult, heartbreaking day, and described for her how it felt like a transaction we were being processed through. I recalled the sights and smells, the busyness and the distraction, and our feeling that we were on a production line – get the new resident admitted, complete the piles of paperwork, check the boxes.

With tears in her eyes, she said, "I feel so ashamed because we do that to families every... single... day."

Ty passed away on April 6, 2015, after four years of living in long term care. By now, our kids were 18 and 23-years-old.

During those four years, I visited Ty regularly. The first year, it was almost every day on my way home from work, and weekends. I would also do my best to bring him home Friday night to Sunday afternoon, until I couldn't.

By the second year, I was back to my regular work travel schedule. With the recommendation from my therapist and support of his family, I slowly decreased the number of visits until it was on average two to three times a week. It was hard to make this shift, partly because I felt guilty about not going. After all, I'm not the one living in a nursing home. I'm the healthy and able one. And yet, my health was starting to suffer due to the stress and strain of my many competing roles.

My role as Ty's wife had changed significantly, from being a couple and parents, to now being his caregiver, advocate, and visiting companion. I was also now in essence a single parent, trying to help our kids cope with seeing their dad living in a care home, slowly withering away. On top of all of that, I was doing my best to fulfil the responsibilities and expectations as an executive, leading my team, and managing my career.

I already knew the risk of burnout that family caregivers have when it comes to their own emotional and physical health. If I wanted to be around to take care of our kids, I needed to invest in my own self-care as best I could.

This wasn't a situation Ty and I, or our kids for

that matter, had ever anticipated or prepared for. We didn't sign up for this. And yet, this was our reality. Resistance, resentment, frustration, and denial weren't going to help us.

During those four years, I proactively sought out support through therapy, reading insightful books, and finding ways to choose my thoughts, feelings, and actions. Yes, some days it was easier said than done. Other days, I could appreciate the happy, more positive moments I got to enjoy with Ty. Even though this wasn't part of our life plan. But this was our life. For now.

While I have some sad memories, I choose to cherish the happy, funny, even delightful memories this journey had in store for us. I want to encourage you to look for the bright spots as well. Know that your presence and partnership in this LTC community matters. Despite the circumstances, I wish for you to have the best possible experience. For you to find a way to contribute, connect, and create moments that matter. Now what? Let's dive in.

CHAPTER 2

The Knowledge Gap

Think about meeting someone for the first time. What do you already know about them? What assumptions or judgments have you made? What kinds of questions do you have? And what are you hoping for?

Similarly, you are now meeting and getting to know the care team members in your LTC home. You don't yet know each other, and it takes time, energy and desire to build a connection. You are at the beginning of what will be an important relationship – one with the team members who will be taking care of your loved one every single day, and you're counting on them.

But in the beginning, there are many things you don't know about the people who will be caring for your loved one, the home, how things work there, and what to expect. You have a knowledge gap. Increasing your knowledge will help generate a higher level of comfort and trust in this new arrangement. That knowledge also applies to the care team who are just as keenly interested in also closing the knowledge gap concerning you and your loved one, as they welcome you into their community.

Closing this knowledge gap should be a common goal for families and care teams. This is where your partnership with them begins, as each of you has what the other needs from a knowledge perspective.

As a family member of a new resident, you'll most likely want to develop a positive relationship with the people who are providing care for your loved one. They also want to provide reassurance that you've made the right decision. They want this to be a positive, healthy relationship. Their goal is for you to be partners in care with their new resident, your loved one.

I want to share a bit of the "behind the scenes" as it relates to your admission day from the home's perspective.

For the care team members, managing admissions is a key part of the daily operations of LTC. It's a process that a mid-sized home does once or twice a week. The reason for this frequency is because on average, about 50% of the resident population changes every year due to relocation or death. This means that every year, about half of the residents in the home are new.

The admission process is lengthy and time consuming. When I work with my clients to help them map out all of the steps - from the time the bed is available (because the previous resident has passed away or has transferred out of the home) to the care conference which occurs about four to six weeks after the admission day, there are approximately 100 different steps involved for the home. This includes reviewing a resident's file submission, approving the application and communicating with those involved in placement, preparing the resident's room, educating the care team about their new resident's clinical and emotional needs, liaising with doctors and others in the care team, not to mention complying with all the regulatory requirements set out by the government.

When the actual admission day arrives, the resident and family come to the home to complete all the paperwork and move their loved one's belongings in. This process involves various care team members and several hours to complete. At the same time, they have other residents to care for. Sometimes it can feel like they are squeezing your admission meeting into an already busy day. They feel the pressure of "processing a new admission" while still needing to do the rest of their job that day. Families can also feel like they are being processed, much like how I felt on Ty's admission day.

As part of the application process, you needed to provide a great deal of information about your loved one. Most of this information is clinical but it feels very personal. The care team needs to verify what medications your loved one is taking and as much information as possible about their medical history.

The care team will have already reviewed the clinical information in the initial application to the home but unfortunately, this kind of information gives a fairly one-dimensional picture of your loved one and sometimes the information is not up-to-date. That's why it's important to fully disclose any health complexities or changes– both physical and emotional – even beyond the introductory, clinical information they may ask for.

If the care team doesn't understand the full picture of who your loved one is, their emotional and physical health, as well as any other relevant information, then a knowledge gap will exist between you and them. This gap can hinder their ability to provide the highest quality of care for your loved one.

Think of it this way: You know your loved one's likes and dislikes and what they did for a living before retiring or needing to move into LTC. You know what they're afraid of and what they enjoy. You know so much about them that their new caregivers don't know – yet. You know a lot about your loved one as well as your family dynamics and relationships, including the dysfunctions. (Yes, I said it. We all have varying degrees of family challenge, conflict, and dysfunction. I used to joke with my kids that it wasn't a matter of **if** they would need therapy one day; it was what they would need therapy for.)

What you may not be aware of is that families (sometimes unintentionally) bring their dysfunction into the home. This can create stress and anxiety for the staff members who are taking care of your loved one.

Dysfunction as well as challenging family dynamics are examples of the type of additional information that is helpful for staff to know about. For example, a home may have to manage sibling rivalry between the children of a resident and who is and isn't entitled to health information. It can get quite sticky for staff if a family member who does not have a power of attorney (POA) comes to visit and challenges the care provider for not sharing health updates. (I expand on this in Chapter 15 Common Misconceptions #18.)

On the other side of the knowledge gap is the care team, who know everything about their home that you don't yet know.

The care team knows the daily rhythm of their home. They know the people who work there and how they work and get along – or not. They know where everything is. They know the other residents and their families. They know which programs the residents really like. They know their place, people, processes, policies, and protocols. They know how things work in their home like the back of their hand.

You have a great deal of knowledge about your loved one that they need, and they have a lot of knowledge about the home that you need.

Think of this need for shared knowledge as a Venn diagram, in which what you know and what the care team knows intersect. The bigger that shared intersecting space, the greater the alignment and understanding between you and the care team. There's less room for unmet expectations, ineffective communication and misunderstandings.

Quality care and life experience

However, both parties are coming at this from different places and different perspectives. The power within the intersection is the shared knowing of what you both want:

For your loved one to experience the best quality care and life experience while living in their long term care home.

CHAPTER 3

Admission Anxiety

There's another shared experience both families and care teams have in common at the beginning of the relationship. It's something I call "Admission Anxiety."

Let's start with your perspective. Let's face it, this is a huge life change, one that's likely to take three months or longer to adjust and adapt to. You've probably already travelled a long and arduous road through the health care system to get to this point. This is what most see as the final transition for their loved one's care, for the rest of their life.

It is a heart-wrenching experience that requires the transacting of documents and completion of paperwork and it can feel like you're being "processed." As I mentioned in the previous chapter, a home may have multiple admissions every week. And since there are no slow days in

LTC, it can feel transactional or rushed because of all the other priorities the staff tend to each day.

Families and Care Teams both experience Admission Anxiety

I didn't know this at the time of Ty's admission. I wonder if it would have allowed me to feel more empathy for the care team and be less judgmental of my experience. Ty had a complex and rare disease. They may have spent a great deal of time trying to understand Ty's condition so that they could be best prepared to help him. He was a younger resident and that in itself can bring other complexities to the situation.

I also hadn't given any thought about how staff were feeling about the resident who had just passed away, creating the opening for Ty's admission.

As much as we felt admission anxiety on this day, the care team members were also feeling their own admission anxiety.

As we sized up these care team members and answered their many questions and processed their instructions, they were sizing us up as well.

Did you know that staff are assessing from their first interaction with new families, trying to figure out where they'll fall on the scale of "how will we get along?" Team members are wondering how much a new family will be a pleasure to deal with or if they'll be a challenge. They wonder if they will be appreciative and grateful, or looking for what's wrong.

This is in part because of the Admission Anxiety the care team feels. After all, this is a new relationship for them as well.

Let me say here that while it's important to bring forward concerns and complaints, it's equally important to do so in a respectful and appropriate way. When there are bursts of emotion that spiral into messy and unproductive conflict, the relationship starts to erode, and your concerns may never be truly resolved. I'll share more about this in the chapter about Accountability.

As part of my consulting work in seniors' care, I conduct focus groups with families, and we talk about how they were feeling at various points during their admission experience. For example, I ask families how it felt when they got the call telling them there was a bed available. We also talk about how they felt when they brought their loved one to the home to move in. Families share how it felt after they left and returned to their home without their loved one.

Here are some memories from families about their admission day experience:

"I'm worried for my mother and scared she won't like being here, or the staff won't be nice to her and know what she needs and likes."

....

"It was a lot of information all at once. It was overwhelming and confusing."

....

"I wish I had another family member or staff member to hold my hand. They have more experience with this than I obviously do."

....

"I was worried who my mom's roommate would be and if they would get along. I was afraid if it's the right choice. I was afraid for my mom because English is her second language."

"I felt frustrated with the paperwork and lack of communication between different staff at the home and us. I felt like the staff didn't explain things thoroughly or were honest with us about our expectations."

....

"It was a great experience – best we could have asked for. I was in tears and sad, and the staff comforted me, which was appreciated."

....

"I felt comfortable when having lunch with everyone on the first day. They took my dad around to meet everyone. The staff was welcoming and friendly, which made me feel more at ease."

....

"I felt relieved, but very sad when I walked into the home I shared with my wife. Now it's empty."

....

"So much anxiety after leaving and going to an empty home."

"I'm happy that my mom is now safe. There was a lot of anxiety having her at home – constantly afraid she will fall down the stairs, fall in the shower, or leave the home. Having her somewhere where she is taken care of made us feel at peace."

....

As you can see, families feel a range of emotions from anxious, nervous, worried, and scared, to relieved, content, and grateful for what is a big day for them and their loved one. Just days before, they got the call saying a bed was available and they had mere hours to decide if they would accept it. Who knows how long a family had been on the waitlist? Or how they've been hanging on, trying to cope and keep up day-to-day care for their loved one.

To varying degrees, most families experience admission anxiety, even when admission to LTC brings some caregiver relief. This can be a highly emotional experience and being aware of the complexities and challenges and knowing you're not alone can help you navigate through it with more confidence and support.

I also conduct focus groups with front line care team members and ask them to share how they feel during the admission experience.

Here are some recollections from them about preparing for the admission day with the new resident and their family:

....

"It's heart-wrenching to put family in a nursing home. I feel that they need reassurance, comforting and support."

....

"I feel worried that the family won't feel satisfied with the care."

....

"We don't know what to expect with the resident's mental state."

....

"Sometimes I feel worried, not because of the resident, but their family members."

....

"Confused as we have to get to know a new resident's likes, dislikes and culture."

"I feel supported by the family because they are giving information for care of their family member."

....

"I worry how the family will react having a loved one in the home – I try to support and reassure them."

....

"I feel frustrated when families want things done that aren't possible. They expect more than we can do."

....

As I've listened to families and care team members share their emotions around this critical time, the anxiety that both feel is palpable. Yet, I think this can be an opportunity to connect through the shared admission anxiety, to show patience, empathy and consideration for each other's perspective, experience, and emotional state during this time.

CHAPTER 4

The Relational Triangle

I'd like you to think about your role as a family member as one of three points of a triangle. There are three key roles that need to work in unison with each other in order to help make this transition and ongoing relationships as smooth as possible.

Think of this as a relational triangle. One that involves interdependency in order to balance expectations, understanding, and trust.

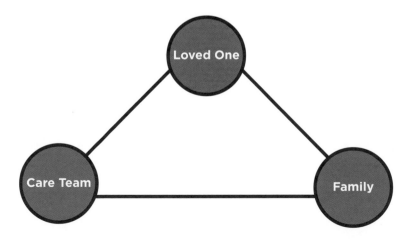

Each person in these roles has expectations and is dependent on the other.

The family is depending on their loved one to let them know how they're feeling, and what they're thinking. They're looking for ways to best support their loved one in their new living environment.

There's also the need for the family to be advocates to ensure their loved one's needs and wants are being heard and responded to by the care team members.

The family is depending on the care team to provide quality care and communicate with them with updates and any other helpful information. They want to know that the care team does CARE about their loved one. After all, families want team members to be happy, warm, and loving while providing care.

The care team is depending on the resident to let them know how they're feeling and what they're thinking – to communicate their needs and wants when or if possible.

The care team is depending on the family to provide relevant information from their perspective in what they see and hear, to share any concerns in an appropriate way, and to connect with both their loved one and care team members as partners in care.

The care team members have their own expectations within this relational triangle. They are human beings doing a job that, for the most part, they feel called to do. They have good days and bad days, just like the rest of us. As they journey through their day, and are working with you and your loved one, the care team members are also looking for ways to make life better for your loved one while getting all of their tasks done. While they have been influenced by their experiences with previous residents and families, they are hopeful and eager to build healthy relationships with your loved one and with you.

It's also important to reflect on the role of the resident – your loved one. They are depending on the care team for physical and emotional support. To do what's reflected in their care plan and to be gentle, caring, compassionate, and patient human beings.

Your loved one is dependant on their family to be there for them. To be many levels of support as desired and needed. This can include some of the task-oriented things like providing clothing and toiletries. It can also be to visit and enjoy each other's company, to be physically and emotionally present, to reassure and comfort.

Your loved one's life has been turned upside down as they are trying to adapt and adjust to this new home where they are likely going to live for the rest of their life. The life they built and knew is transitioning into a new chapter.

In *Transitions: Making Sense of Life's Changes*, author William Bridges writes about the importance of navigating transitions in our lives. He believes every transition begins with an ending and ends with a beginning. For your loved one, living independently, likely with better health, has now ended. What has begun is this new life in long term care. Bridges identified five stages in the ending process: disengagement, dismantling, disidentification, disenchantment, and disorientation.

If you are interested in learning more about this, I highly recommend his book. For purposes of highlighting it here, my point is that your loved one is also on an emotional journey with this life change. How they are thinking and feeling about it will impact the experience for both you as a family member and for the care team in the home.

All three points of this Relational Triangle impact and influence each other.

It's important to keep in mind that the only person that you can control...is you. You have agency over your thoughts, feelings, and behaviours. You can choose to be intentional with how you show up.

You cannot control the thoughts, feelings, and behaviours of those around you (as much as we would really like to some days!).

However, you can impact and influence the thoughts, feelings, and behaviours of others with your choices in how you relate to them. How you choose to show up. How you choose to interact with them.

In order to be more thoughtful and intentional in your role and how you can influence and impact others, it's important to recognize the various touchpoints you will experience as a family member. We'll talk more about this journey in the Seven A's in the next chapter.

THE
SEVEN
A's

CHAPTER 5

The Seven A's

L et's face it, transitioning into becoming a resident's family member is not for the faint of heart. This is not only a big change logistically, but also an emotional experience that you are likely not prepared for.

I have walked this journey personally and counselled countless families on their journey. As unique as everyone's experience is, there are also many similarities. I reflected on the many conversations I had and from that developed the framework of the Seven A's. These are touchpoints to help give you insight and guidance on your journey.

These touchpoints aren't necessarily experienced in a linear way. You may find yourself cycling through them and back – revisiting these touchpoints episodically. Like going through the stages of grief, I don't think it's a "one and done" experience. The journey evolves as your loved one's condition changes and as you become more familiar with your role and as a member in this community.

My hope for you is to develop insight, experience comfort, and build a foundation to come back to when you are feeling uncertain, anxious, or frustrated with your role as a family member.

The next seven chapters expand on each of these touchpoints on the emotional journey. They are:

AWARE
Recognizing that things have changed
to the point that it's time to make
a decision.

ACKNOWLEDGE
Recognizing the impact this is having on
you and how you're feeling.

ADAPT
Finding ways to integrate these changes
into your life.

ACCEPT

Acceptance is the prerequisite to change and this is a huge change. When we no longer resist reality and can accept what is, the transition becomes smoother.

ALLOW

It doesn't have to be all bad. This is where you find more opportunities for positivity and expansion in your life through thoughts, feelings, and activities.

ACCOUNTABLE

Your new role as a family member brings certain responsibilities. You'll be accountable for contributing to a working partnership with the home's caregivers.

APPRECIATE

When you're able to see and show gratitude for the moments that matter, the accomplishments, and even the heartache, you'll make memories you can look back on for comfort.

When I look back on my own transitions – with my dad, my husband, then my mom – I can see how I touched on each of these points. Even with my insider knowledge working in the industry, I struggled. Looking back, I realize I didn't know what I didn't know. On multiple occasions, I was blindsided by what I wasn't prepared for.

Let's dig a little deeper into what the various stages represent. We'll explore what you could be thinking about now to feel better prepared for your new role as a family member.

At the end of each chapter are questions that can help navigate you through each of these touchpoints. You may want to pause and think through some or all of the questions. You may also find it helpful to journal your thoughts and feelings in a notebook. I've also provided space in this book to write answers to each question. You may want to use these questions as discussion points with other family members or friends. Or you can highlight questions you want to review with one of the care team members at the home.

It may also be helpful to mark those pages you want to come back to. Remember, this isn't a linear process. You may find yourself cycling forward or back at different points along this journey. What may not feel totally relevant now, may be right on the mark at another time. Use these questions in a way that can best support you with what you need right now.

"Awareness is the
greatest agent
for change."

- Eckhart Tolle -

CHAPTER 6

Aware

Awareness can come in more than one form. It can come from a significant emotional event, or it can come as a more gradual experience. And yet, this is where I think our journey starts – with the awareness that more help is needed, even when we don't know exactly what that is.

My day of awareness came when our case manager said to me, "Deb, you can no longer safely and effectively take care of Ty at home. He needs to be put on the crisis list and placed into long term care."

We lived in a four-level side split home, with stairs from the main floor to the bedrooms. Ty was using a walker and was transitioning to a wheelchair. He was going to an adult day care program a few days a week, as I was working full time with an hour commute each way. The kids were in school, and collectively we were trying to integrate this unimaginable reality into our lives.

I was trying to be all things to all people: wife, mother, caregiver, sister, daughter, manager, colleague. It wasn't going well. I was exhausted and felt like I wasn't doing a great job in any of my roles.

The frequency of Ty's falls was increasing and the home care hours he received just weren't enough. Our entire family was struggling. I think I needed to be told this was no longer safe or sustainable for any of us. I think I needed to be given permission to wave the white flag, surrender, and say "I can't do this anymore." The awareness came from someone looking in who could clearly see the impossibility of the situation and spell it out for me.

With my dad, the awareness was more gradual. I wasn't seeing firsthand the struggle my mom was having with his care. What I saw was how tired she was, while resisting the reality that she couldn't continue to be his primary caregiver without sacrificing her own health and wellbeing. And I think she too needed to be given permission to accept help by moving my dad into long term care.

With my mom, my awareness of her decline happened while she lived in retirement after my dad passed away. She was also having falls. She was making mistakes with her medications and the staff had to take over the responsibility of dispensing medication to her. She wound up in the hospital after another fall and that was the beginning of her more noticeable physical and cognitive decline.

The awareness that my mom needed more help was clear, but it still took time to get there. I think in part because all of us were in a bit of denial, including my mom. We saw what we wanted to see, because accepting the reality of our mom's aging and illness was just too much to bear. It was a doctor at the hospital who suggested she needed a higher level of care. We made the decision to move her to another retirement home that had assisted living. She lived there for three years before passing away in the spring of 2019.

There are many ways we arrive at the moments when the harsh reality sets in. Whether that's knowing it's time for long term care, or you're still hanging on by your fingernails taking care of them at home. You likely know, wherever they are, that it's simply not sustainable. Perhaps you notice your own physical and/or mental health is impacted. You lay awake at night wondering how this is all going to play out.

Possibly you've had conversations with the family doctor, specialists, or the health authority and you know a decision needs to be made. You've become aware that something has to change. You've become aware that this is a decision that no one ever really wants to make.

Finally, you make the decision and select your preferred homes. Then you're either put on a waitlist, or the home you chose doesn't have a waitlist. Either way, your loved one's file is reviewed, and you get the phone call saying a bed is available. You have mere hours to accept or decline, otherwise the bed goes to someone else.

You're aware that your loved one needs to be in care. Now it's time to think about what else you need to become more aware of, as well as what you need to know about LTC.

Here are some questions to reflect on and

write your thoughts to help increase your level of
awareness and knowledge:

- *What do I know and not know about
long term care?*

....

....

....

- *What's important for me to know?*

....

....

....

....

- *What's important for me to learn?*

....

....

....

- *What resources can I ask for?*

....

....

....

- *What resources are we eligible for?*

....

....

....

- *How can I prepare my loved one?*

....

....

....

- *Who can help me / us?*

....

....

....

"You can't change what you don't acknowledge."

-Dr. Phil -

CHAPTER 7

Acknowledge

For me, it took sitting across from my therapist to acknowledge the impact this huge life change was having on my physical and emotional well-being.

She recapped for me all that was on my plate: working full time in a senior-level position with a busy schedule and lots of responsibility; a single parent raising two kids who were dealing with their own issues; taking care of a home and all the required maintenance; being Ty's wife, advocate, and partner in care with the staff at the home; being a daughter to my aging parents and supporting my mom as best as I could while my dad's health declined due to Parkinson's and Lewy Body dementia. Never mind my role as a sibling, friend, and neighbour.

Sometimes it's hard for us to see and acknowledge what this change means to us, how it's impacting us, what stories we are telling ourselves about our circumstances, and how we really feel.

This stage is about recognizing and acknowledging the emotional impact this is having on you.

When we have been in tactical mode, juggling medical appointments, arranging care, and working through the logistics, we can compartmentalize and push down any negative feelings. Trust me, I tried it. It's not sustainable.

Then what happens is the emotions come leaking out at the most inopportune times, usually as a disproportionate emotional reaction to something that under normal circumstances wouldn't faze us. Maybe it's losing your temper at another driver who has left their signal on, even though they're not changing lanes. Or bursting into tears because someone asked you how you're feeling, and you aren't sure if you can pull yourself together enough to answer.

For me, therapy gave me a place to unpack what I was really feeling in a safe place, without judgment. I could speak with someone who was well trained to listen to what I was saying and to listen for what I wasn't. She helped me reframe my reality in a way that was palatable, so that I could digest it in bite-sized pieces, rather than choke on the overwhelm and grief.

I also had a girlfriend who called me weekly, just to check in on me, and offer a supportive ear and heart. Not to tell me what to do, or how to feel. Just to listen and acknowledge. And sometimes I would go to a Saturday afternoon movie alone – to escape reality for a couple hours and allow myself to be elsewhere.

It's important we give ourselves permission to sit still, reflect, and consider what's really going on. These questions can help you process your thoughts and feelings:

• *How does this decision make me feel?*

....

....

....

....

- *What emotions do I need to unpack and look more closely at?*

....

....

- *What resources or support do I need to create or have?*

....

....

- *Do I need to forgive myself?*

....

....

- *How can I be gentler with myself?*

....

....

- *How can I give myself some grace?*

....

....

- *How am I telling my story to others?*

....

....

- *How am I telling my story to myself?*

....

....

....

"When we are
no longer able to
change a situation,
we are challenged
to change
ourselves."

- Viktor Frankl -

CHAPTER 8

Adapt

I remember how lonely and surreal it felt to come home and not have Ty there. When we were living together, it was stressful because he needed so much care. On the other hand, witnessing first-hand his gradual decline and our loss as a family made me feel incredibly sad for him and for us.

There was a window of time where I struggled to adapt to this new normal. I think I expected to settle in much more quickly, but it was at least three to four months before I felt like this was our regular routine.

There were spaces of unfilled time and fewer responsibilities. We no longer had PSW's (Personal Support Workers) coming in each morning and afternoon. It was quieter. Calmer. But in an unsettling way. My kids and I weren't used to it. Nor were we used to driving to Ty's new home and everything that represented.

I had to remind myself that I was now a resident's spouse and when I went to visit him, I was a family member in this new community. I needed to adapt to this new role and title, as well as the new routines and requirements to raise our kids as a single parent. I was not only visiting Ty regularly, but also spending time getting to know the people working there who were taking care of him.

Adapting is about how you integrate all of these changes into your life. The changes in roles, living arrangements, travelling, family celebrations, and losses.

This is an opportunity to consider what these changes will look like from a practical perspective. How do you plan to structure your days, with all the activities and chores that need to be done?

Another thing to consider is your visiting schedule, including the frequency and length of visits. Determine what's the best time to visit, based on their new schedule and yours. Will you want to spend time doing activities together? Sitting to enjoy a cup of coffee and catch up? Or help with personal care or other kinds of support, like helping them get dressed and personal grooming. Some families like to be more involved with personal care, or mealtime help, however, it's not the expectation. This is the time to figure out your role and responsibility as your loved one's advocate with the care team.

In addition, how do you ensure that you're also taking care of yourself, your needs, and priorities outside of this role? This is so important and can be easily pushed aside. If you've been the primary caregiver, perhaps you've not had time to make self-care a priority. I can't stress how important it is to have a plan around this and the necessary supports to facilitate it.

This process of adapting has practical components, as I've outlined above. You also have to adapt emotionally as you put these strategies and approaches in place. It can be easy to fall into a robotic state of organizing, arranging, and managing. It helps us feel useful and productive. It's also important to take the time to pause and reflect on how you are feeling as you go through this stage.

You can start by asking yourself these questions:

- *What are MY needs?*

....

....

- *What's most important to me throughout my responsibilities and this new role?*

....

....

- *What, and who can help me integrate this new role into my life in a healthy and balanced way?*

....

....

....

....

- *What can I stop doing, or let go of, to make room for this new reality?*

....

....

- *What can I start doing to help with this adjustment?*

....

....

- *Who can I share my feelings and experiences with to feel supported?*

....

....

This can be an ideal time to incorporate self-care practices like meditation, exercise, massage therapy, support groups, therapy or counselling, and quality sleep. I suspect this isn't the first time you've heard this from your circle of family and friends, yet it is so important to take seriously. My mother used to say, "your health is your wealth," and she was a very wise woman!

"We cannot change
anything unless we
accept it."

- Carl Jung -

CHAPTER 9

Accept

In hindsight, I resisted the identity of being a resident's wife for some time. Certainly, Ty being a younger resident was a contributing factor. (In Canada, only about 10% - 12% of residents in LTC are under the age of 65.) I mean, here were my kids dealing with the reality that it was their dad, not their grandfather, they were visiting in a nursing home. None of their peers could relate to how that was for them. As well, at my age, none of my friends had spouses living in long term care.

When I visited homes as part of my job, I would inevitably see a younger resident that reminded me of Ty and my eyes would well up with tears, thinking how unfair all of this really was.

I was trying to manage my anger and sadness over this significant loss while trying to keep my game face on for everybody at work, my kids, and Ty's new home, which he shared with 143 other residents.

I needed to start accepting this situation. This was my new reality and my family was never going back to our old "normal." This was it. Like it or not.

Here's the thing with acceptance. It doesn't mean that we have to love or even like the situation we're in. We can, however, let go of the resistance, frustration, and resentment for the situation we feel we've been put in.

When we truly accept that this is the best option considering the reality of our loved one's condition and need, this can free up a lot of our emotional energy to be more resourceful, positive and influential.

It may not come easily or quickly. But I believe it's a necessary step in permitting yourself to let go of those thoughts and feelings that aren't serving you, and those around you, including your loved one.

Here are some reflective questions to help with moving toward acceptance:

- *What do I need to let go of?*

....

....

- *What can I embrace?*

....

....

- *How can I accomplish this?*

....

....

....

- *Who can I lean on that's been through this?*

....

....

- *What assumptions am I making that just aren't true?*

....

....

- *How can I look at things differently?*

....

....

....

....

- *What positive things can I identify about this situation?*

....

....

- *What can I embrace?*

....

....

- *How can I accomplish this?*

....

....

....

Remember, you don't have to like something in order to accept it.

"The sooner we let go of holding on, the sooner we can hold on to the beauty of what's unfolding before us. Nothing was ever meant to stay the same forever."

- Julieanne O'Connor -

CHAPTER 10

Allow

Ty was a handsome and charming gentleman (one of the many reasons I married him) and he maintained those qualities even during his illness. He was extroverted, loved being with people and participating in the home's activities. Bingo night became one of his rituals. He made everyone laugh and was fun to be around.

One evening after work I swung by the home to visit him. We had argued the night before. (Yes, even through illness, couples can still fight!) and I wanted to pop in to see how he was doing.

In the main entrance area, the bingo tables were set up and Ty was sitting with a group of ladies. It became clear to me that he had shared our friction-filled conversation from the night before. They were all on Ty's side...and as I walked toward his table, I got the stink eye from the entire group of elderly women!

When I look back on this event, I realize that I was in a place of allowing. I could see the humour in the situation. I could appreciate that he was making friends. It was really nice to see him getting more involved with the activities and events that the home offered. He didn't need me there as often, and sometimes I even wondered if I was 'cramping his style' at times. I wondered if he'd rather be going to the home's pub night and enjoying a beer with his buddies.

I was able to allow the gratitude and I learned to appreciate these little moments that were now a part of our new normal. I was also able to connect with other families and not just talk about our loved one's condition, or how hard it was. We learned more about each other and shared updates about what was going on in our lives, outside of the home. Our conversations became supportive and relational.

This is where magical moments can happen. Through the acceptance stage, you release some of the emotions that perhaps were keeping you stuck in that place of frustration and resentment. Toxic emotions that are not dealt with, have the potential to create serious physical and emotional issues.

This is the stage where you can see possibilities and opportunities to contribute. Perhaps you'll even begin to enjoy your new role and become a valuable part of this new community. You can choose to make memorable and meaningful moments to brighten someone else's day with a smile, or a touch. You may have a conversation with another family member that seems coincidental and strike up a friendship. When you allow, you are shifting your energy to become more open and engaging.

- *What can I create out of this?*

....

....

....

....

- *What opportunities can I explore?*

....

....

....

- *What possibilities can open up?*

....

....

....

- *What can I allow to happen?*

....

....

....

- *What relationships can flourish?*

....

....

....

- *How can I brighten someone's day?*

....

....

....

- *What am I grateful for?*

....

....

....

"We are all responsible and accountable for what we do or say even if those behaviours occur in stressful times."

- Byron Pulsifer -

CHAPTER 11

Accountable

My first impression of the home and team from Ty's admission day experience wasn't very positive. Remember, I had experience working in LTC, so I had more knowledge than most about the requirements and how busy homes are. But as a family member, focused on my pain and grief, I felt very unsettled and concerned about how Ty would be cared for. I also wondered how they would support me and the kids.

Remember, the care team also feel anxious before a new resident moves in. They may be grieving the death of a resident that they took care of and grew to love. Meanwhile, they need to prepare to welcome the new resident, while knowing little about that person.

But what tends to make the care team even more anxious is wondering what the new family is going to be like. Will they be a pleasure to deal with? Will they be patient and understanding? Will they be challenging? Will they have unrealistic expectations of team members?

Every family experiences a myriad of emotions about this move. Most families I've discussed this with felt anxious and nervous about the decision. They worry that their loved ones won't want to stay. Some families even tell their loved one that "it's just a visit" and that creates a whole other set of challenges for the staff when the family leaves their loved one there with all of their belongings. Others worry about the level of care their loved ones are going to get and of letting go of the control they had over caring for their loved one. I've even heard of families worrying that their loved ones will do better without them. The range of emotions and concerns are as varied as each family. Yet the common thread of anxiety tends to exist.

The success of being "partners in care" is a two-way street. I believe both the care team members and families have a role to play in contributing positively to the relationship. This starts with that very first impression and assessment of each other. It continues to grow with each interaction you have with each other, whether it's sharing a compliment, a concern, seeking insight, or information.

Think of it like making deposits into the relational bank account that you share with the care team. As this account grows, so does the trust. The confidence. The respect you have for each other.

This means as a family member you are accountable for how you show up, engage with, and relate to all the care team members, as well as other residents and families. You are now part of this community. True, you don't live here, but you do spend time visiting. Your presence impacts the culture of the home. It also impacts the lives of those who work, live, and visit there.

It takes both sides of the "partners in care" to focus on enhancing the relationship through understanding, collaboration, care, and support for each other.

I think it's safe to say that there will be situations where you are going to be disappointed. Your expectations won't be met. There will be misunderstandings. In any relationship that matters, stuff happens that creates tension. It's how we respond - versus react - to the situation and the person that will shape the outcome.

Reset with PORCH in Chapter 13 provides a practical way to ground yourself. That way you're in a better position to be responsive, versus reactive, particularly when emotions may be charged. Typically, when we let our emotions get the better of us, we say and do things that could cause harm and regret.

In my first book *RECIPE for Empathy,* one of the chapters is called "Curiosity: The Question Connection." I share how being curious can actually help cancel out judgment and anger. When we can be truly curious about a situation, or another person's behaviour, it doesn't allow space to make assumptions and create stories based on our worries and fears. Being curious then sparks questions with a desire to understand and see the full picture.

Grounding yourself and coming from a place of curiosity are two examples of approaches you can practice in your role as a family member.

Consider these questions to help you reflect further on your family member role:

- *What responsibilities do I have in this situation?*

....

....

....

....

- *How do I want and need to show up as a community member and partner?*

....

....

....

....

- *How will I manage my emotions, needs, and concerns?*

....

....

....

- *How do I respectfully communicate my questions or concerns?*

....

....

....

- *How can I respond, versus react, when a challenge occurs?*

....

....

....

• *Have I effectively shared my expectations with the care team and are they realistic and achievable?*

....

....

....

• *How can I help to build trust in these relationships?*

....

....

....

"Gratitude makes sense of your past, brings peace for today, and creates a vision for tomorrow."

- Melody Beattie -

CHAPTER 12

Appreciate

The home Ty moved into was our top choice. I was grateful he wasn't on the crisis list for too long before we got the call to say they had a room for him.

Just because we got the home that was our number one choice, it didn't mean everything was perfect all the time. There were many situations, from lost clothing, to broken reading glasses to other misunderstandings that happened. This is part of transitioning into a community setting with many other residents and care team members.

It was helpful to remind myself what our lives looked like those weeks and months before Ty was accepted and moved in. Ty's disease was progressing and his abilities, both physical and cognitive, would continue to decline. Even though I couldn't know what that would look like, I did know that it would become impossible for me to take care of him at home. And my health was already being negatively impacted. My kids, who were completely dependent on me, were worried about my ability to stay healthy and keep everything together. I was sleep deprived, losing weight and at one point through my fatigue, fell down a flight of stairs in our home and broke my wrist (my dominant hand, of course) which needed a cast for six weeks.

This stage of appreciation can be tricky, but it can be incredibly powerful. It can be tricky because of the challenge you face in embracing grief and gratitude. It's hard to imagine feeling both states simultaneously. I cried tears of sadness when I watched Ty, sitting in his wheelchair in a circle with other residents, playing a tambourine in a music therapy class. Ty would be mortified if he could see himself like this. And the tears were also filled with gratitude that he WAS enjoying this music circle, creating songs with his friends, being in the moment and forgetting about everything else.

You can get to a place where you can see some of the gifts that have risen out of your grief, guilt, and all the other emotions you may have felt at the beginning of this journey. Some feel gratitude for being accepted into the home of their choice after a long time on a waitlist. Others may feel grateful that they can get a better night's sleep knowing their loved one is in good hands and is being well cared for. You may appreciate the new friends you've been able to meet while visiting. Once you're better able to manage your grief and guilt, you may also feel really appreciative of being able to take time for yourself, outside of this caregiving role.

It's also important to notice and appreciate the kindness and generosity of your care team. It may sound cliché, but one kind word can change someone's entire day.

The work they do isn't easy. They work in a life and death business. They support many residents, families, and each other. They hear the concerns and complaints, but not so much the compliments and acknowledgements.

The team work very closely with your loved one, not just with their physical care needs, but their emotional needs as well. They share hugs and smiles. They get to know their idiosyncrasies. They know what makes them laugh, and what makes them cry. They see your loved one as part of their community family. They do their best to take care of them.

It's an opportunity to look for these little moments that matter, and to express your appreciation and gratitude for the work they do, the care they provide, and the compassion they share. A little gratitude can go a long way. It's another way to make deposits into your relational bank account.

I want to share something that care team members do outside the scope of their job which I think is pretty incredible. There are residents who don't have families, or their families aren't available. There are residents who don't get visitors or anyone to buy new clothing or Christmas presents for them. They are not forgotten by the care team. Staff will raise funds or use their own money to purchase comfort items and gifts for these residents. They care about their residents and want them to know that they are loved.

Here are some questions to help you reflect on appreciation and gratitude:

- *What are some possible silver linings here?*

....

....

....

....

- *What can I choose to focus on?*

....

....

....

....

• *What and who can I be grateful for?*

....

....

....

....

....

• *How can I share my gratitude with those who are supporting me?*

....

....

....

....

....

- *What really matters here?*

....

....

....

....

....

CHAPTER 13

Reset with PORCH

I wrote *RECIPE for Empathy* for people who work in seniors' care. I wanted to provide a framework to help transform their residents' families into fans.

After I wrote the book, I received an email from a reader about one of the tools I developed called PORCH (It's an acronym for Pause, Observe, Reflect, Choose, Happen). PORCH is a way to reset yourself by intentionally shifting your focus so that you can respond – versus react – when your emotions may be getting the better of you. The woman who wrote to me didn't work in health care but was a family member with both of her parents living in seniors' care.

"Imagine if every seniors' care home only applied PORCH, the shift would bring trust between the family and care team. I would feel so hopeful and less anxious if I knew my mother's interactions with

the care team were filled with empathy. Having said all that, the biggest learning was that I needed to make some shifts myself in my expectations and attitude. I now change my energy when I walk through the doors of the home. I smile at everyone I meet and say hello.

I am determined to show up and be present and not just look for what is wrong, but also acknowledge what is working. I take time to notice the nursing and cleaning staff and their hard work. I apply PORCH and other methods in the book to help with creating relationships based on understanding.

This is a must-read for every health care worker, administrator, nurse, and every family member."

This email prompted me to include PORCH in this book. Let me start by explaining why resetting is important and how it can help you.

You are likely a pretty busy person. Now you've had to figure out how to adjust your life and lifestyle to align with your new identity as a family member supporting a loved one living in a seniors' care home.

I recall heading into the home to visit Ty and my mind was still spinning with all of my work to do's that didn't get done. I had sandwiched the visit between driving home from a one-hour commute, to needing to be home to make dinner for the kids.

I was doing to Ty what I felt the care team members were doing to us on his admission day. I was squeezing in a visit in an already busy day. I was being transactional. Also, I was half present at that. My body was there, but my mind was elsewhere.

I was already feeling pressure, a bit agitated, and in a hurry. Then, I see that he hasn't been shaved that day. He tells me he pulled the call bell "hours ago," but no one came.

Or I'd go see my mom at the home she was in and I could tell she probably needed help getting changed from her pyjamas into her day clothes. The blind that was broken in her room—the one I kept bugging them to fix—was still laying there, crumpled on the floor.

In both of these instances, I wasn't in the best frame of mind to begin with. I experienced something that annoyed me. Then I got reactive. I likely reacted disproportionately to the situation, expressed my anger rather passionately, and chipped away at the respect and trust in my relationship with the people who were caring for my husband and my mother.

As with any dynamic, it's helpful to have a framework we can access when mindfulness, courtesy, and patience feels inaccessible to us in that moment.

The PORCH framework can help to pull you out of the "going reactive and causing damage" mode into a more thoughtful, productive place.

....

P: PAUSE

When frustration turns to anger, stress hormones start coursing through your body. Take a few seconds to take two or three deep breaths. This pause lets your nervous system know everything is okay. You're not in danger, but you want to calm your nervous system so that you don't go right into fight or flight mode. It can prevent you from immediately reacting and acting in a way that would be unhelpful and hurtful for you, your loved one, or the person providing care.

O: OBSERVE

As you're breathing, observe yourself. Your role right now is to notice and observe what you're feeling, where you're feeling it, and name the emotion. Observe yourself and your emotions and reactions without judgment. This can take a few moments and is important in being able to self-regulate and use reasoning to problem solve.

Then, as you approach the care provider and engage them in conversation and ask questions related to your concerns, continue to observe. Notice how your words are impacting them, as this will have a direct influence on the quality of discussion and the outcome. Watch the conversation as if you're in the audience, even though you're engaged with them.

This helps you to maintain perspective, which can be hard to see when you're emotionally charged.

····························

R: REFLECT

Perhaps at this point you've been able to share your concern with the care team member and you've also been able to hear their response, and maybe even have a better understanding of the situation. Or you may still be unclear. Since you've worked to keep yourself in a calm state and have taken in information through observation, you can now reflect and sort through the information you have.

Ask yourself: Are things resolved? Do you have a better understanding of the situation? If not, what other options do you have to work towards a resolution? You will be better able to access your critical thinking at this stage, as you have preserved your energy and focus through a calm, collected approach.

·····························

C: CHOOSE

This is where you're able to make a choice as to your next step. Choose your response based on what you've been able to gather through the previous three steps of Pause, Observe, and Reflect. By remaining calm and open, you're better able to tap into your perspective, as well as your knowledge of the situation, before choosing how to respond.

H: MAKE IT HAPPEN

After effectively pausing, observing, reflecting, and choosing the right next step it's time to take action in a positive and constructive way.

You may find yourself naturally or instinctively applying these steps when you have the bandwidth to respond. By bandwidth, I mean the amount of energy you have, or how well you're functioning in that moment. Being well-rested, feeling centred, and able to focus all build support into your available bandwidth. This relates to your ability to clearly see that space between stimulus (what just happened) and response (how you're dealing with it).

In reaction mode, it can be difficult to suspend time for a few moments and take advantage of an observing space. Liken it to sitting in the audience and observing, versus being on stage immersed in the drama. When you're able to pause, you can observe what's happening while simultaneously noticing how you're feeling in the moment. You're better able to evaluate the clarity and quality of your thinking and then make choices that will support the outcome you want to create.

This PORCH framework can give you that two second beat between stimulus and response to catch your breath and reset yourself. Then you can more effectively use the space that Viktor Frankl referenced in this quote:

"**Between stimulus and response there is a space. In that space is our power to choose our response.**
In our response lies our growth and our freedom."

By being intentional with how you choose to respond (versus react) you are increasing your chances of having better relationships, while preserving your energy and emotions to create more positive experiences.

CHAPTER 14

What's your Family Flavour?

Every family that comes to LTC arrives with their own uniqueness and story. The main reason families come through the door is usually due to a loved one's health crisis that is significant enough to require full time care. Whether that person is your parent, spouse, sibling, adult child, or friend, their condition is assessed, and this solution is offered as your best choice.

This got me thinking about the different kinds of families who become part of an LTC community. And with this, the variety of ways that families cope with their decision to place their loved one in long term care, and how well they adapt to the changes it creates in their lifestyle and family dynamics.

When I worked in LTC, I heard many stories about conflict between care team members and families. When I was in my role as a family member,

I could look back and notice how my behaviour changed depending on the kind of day I had, or how a concern got resolved...or not. I also saw this with the many families I worked with, as they shared their stories about LTC and how they were coping - or not - with the decision.

Similarly, there can also be different flavours or layers of complexity – even within the same family. Those variations can impact the relationship with the care team.

Much like when we cook meals that have a predominant flavour, family members can also have a signature "flavour." For example, if you're making chili, it can be mild, or you could enhance the flavour with various spices and extra hot peppers.

Let me explain. I work with many clients who are leaders and frontline care providers in long term care homes. They share with me what great family relationships look and feel like. My clients also share what challenging and difficult family relationships look and feel like to them.

Over time, I started to notice a pattern with these stories. Common themes started to emerge. I realized families fell into one of three different styles in terms of how they communicate, relate and work with others.

This made me reflect on how I showed up as a family member when both my parents and my husband were in LTC and Assisted Living. I could see myself reflected in these styles, which I refer to as "family flavours."

Before we get into the three types, I want to preface it with a few thoughts:

I believe families tend to be most like one of the three flavours outlined below the majority of the time. This is their default setting. However, it doesn't mean things can't get a little spicy; their flavour profile can change, depending on the situation they're in. It could be that some issues in the home don't bother them, while other situations can be a real trigger. Think of someone who isn't fussed about missing laundry for their loved one but gets upset if they aren't participating in enough activities. But generally speaking, this is how they show up.

You can also have all three flavours within one family. For example, a resident may have two children, each with their own personality style and distinct role as their parent's advocate,

Power of Attorney, or primary caregiver. This role can influence their presence in the home and how they communicate with and relate to the care providers. The other factor is their pre-existing relationship with their loved one. They may have been taking care of them in their home, or they lived hours away and didn't have much of a role with the day-to-day care. There are many factors that influence the "flavour" of each family member.

Understand this section isn't about judging anyone. I know better than most there are times when we go with the flow and other times when we get hot under the collar. Instead, I want to share with you what I've observed. That way, you can consider how you want to show up and interact with the care team members who work at the home and whose job it is to take care of your loved one.

Finally, each individual team member also has a responsibility in how he or she shows up and interacts with the families. Reflecting back on the reset tool, PORCH, staff also need to recognize when they're feeling stressed or triggered. Then they too need to take appropriate steps to manage their emotions and maintain a professional attitude and response with families.

This is an opportunity to see how you can show up and the kind of presence you want to have when visiting your loved one and interacting with your care providers.

....

1. SALT AND PEPPER

This tends to be the majority of families. Some of these families aren't physically present in the home as often. Perhaps they live a distance away, are still working full time, or raising kids.

If you are a Salt and Pepper, the care team members may recognize you when you come in to visit but may not know as much about you and your family.

Generally speaking, the Salt and Peppers are fairly laid back and tend to trust and appreciate the work the team members are doing. This type of family certainly asks questions as things come up and seeks answers to bring them comfort and a better understanding of how things work in the home. Salt and Peppers like to be kept informed of things. If they feel they're "in the know," they're happy.

I was primarily a Salt and Pepper. I was working and parenting. I would visit Ty four or five times a week some weeks and others maybe only once or twice, particularly if I was travelling for work. I knew his caregivers and we were friendly with each other. If I had any concerns, I knew which team member I needed to speak with to resolve any issues.

....

2. SWEET AND SAVOURY

Families who are predominantly the Sweet and Savoury flavour are the ones the team members usually love to see when they walk through the front doors. This type of family is typically polite and engaging. They enjoy visiting and chatting with the various people working that day. Sweet and Savouries appreciate the hard work and support the team members provide to their loved ones, while also understanding it's a tough job!

I also think of this type of family as the "influencers." These are the families that know the goings-on in the home almost as well as the staff do. They keep other families abreast with what's going on too. For example, if there's a raffle coming up, or a Karaoke night – Sweet and Savouries are the ones who encourage other families to get involved or perhaps volunteer as well.

This type of family tends to be respectful of the rules and requirements. They've been around long enough to know why the rules are important and why it makes sense to follow them. Sweet and Savouries don't hesitate to ask questions and request opportunities to discuss issues when they arise – approaching the conversation with calmness, curiosity and patience.

They're also the families that will help welcome new families, show them the ropes, and help guide them. They remember what it was like first becoming a family member. The Sweet and Savoury is an ambassador and often a voice of reason when other family members may feel frazzled over something.

I recall a pair of Sweet and Savoury sisters whose dad was a resident on the same floor as my husband. Both women were retired and were probably at the home for two to three hours every day visiting their dad as well as volunteering in the home, helping with other residents. When I first became a family member, they introduced themselves to me, and wanted to know who my loved one was. They also gave me a knowing, reassuring look. The sisters could see my angst but encouraged me to believe that things would be okay. Everyone in the home knew them (kind of like the regulars in Cheers, but different!) and they truly were like part of the entire team. I appreciated the sisters' involvement. Sometimes I'd come in to visit Ty and they'd tell me funny stories about how Ty and their dad were joking around in the dining room. After their dad passed away, both sisters continued to volunteer at that home.

....

3. JALAPENO

This group of families tends to be the smallest percentage of the overall family population. However, they are more likely to take up most of the frontline and management's time. As the name suggests, Jalapenos tend to be hot and spicy to deal with.

Unfortunately, there are families who come in with a preconceived perception of "how bad long term care homes are." They might feel guilty and upset over making the decision to put a loved one into care, which creates a barrier to forming a healthy relationship with the care team. Others may be waiting for something to go wrong, to prove to themselves it wasn't a good idea. This kind of thinking can start the makings of a Jalapeno family. It can be extremely difficult for the home's management and team members to build a strong relationship of trust and partnership when this is how the relationship begins.

I think it's also safe to say that most families will have their Jalapeno moments. This tends to happen if they're caught off guard by something or haven't been updated with information that they deem critical. These moments are easily recoverable from when the family is more like a Jalapeno popper. They're hot, but it subsides. They can reset and reengage and usually are able to acknowledge the unfortunate episode, realizing they probably had an overreaction due to feeling emotionally hijacked.

Here's an example: One family member – let's call her Brenda – shared with me how she was caught off guard when she discovered that her husband was wearing an incontinent brief. This was not a part of his care plan, nor was Brenda asked or informed of this change. Brenda went "Jalapeno popper" on the care team member working that day. She wasn't upset about the brief; she was upset that no one told her; that they just decided it was time for him to wear a brief. And for Brenda, it was another sign that her husband was declining further. Brenda was a Sweet and Savoury family member having a Jalapeno moment.

Within families there can be individuals who represent all three types. As I mentioned previously, most (if not all) families have some level of dysfunction or "baggage" that sometimes becomes apparent in the home. You can have siblings who are supportive and understanding, while others are frustrated and combative. Sometimes it's because of their own internal relationships within the family. Perhaps one holds the Power of Attorney and is the lead decision maker and the other siblings are unhappy with that arrangement. Or one of the daughters was the primary caregiver and is struggling to give up their responsibility. A situation like this would mean care team members must deal with a variety of personalities, preferences, and family flavours all within the same family.

In my experience with the clients I work with, every home has a handful of Jalapeno families. Let's remember that the people who work in LTC are human beings too. They take things personally and can feel defensive and make up their own stories about the family's attitudes and behaviours. Here's what care team members have shared with me about their Jalapeno family experiences:

When they see a Jalapeno family member coming down the hall, they may quickly turn around and head the other way. Why? Because they don't want to deal with yet another confrontation. If you notice that care team members don't want to make eye contact with you (and not because they don't see you or are busy doing something else), or provide brief yes or no responses when you ask questions, you may be perceived as a Jalapeno.

The care team's reactions can also contribute to a perfect storm. When families are aggressive, yelling or speaking to care providers disrespect-fully, they can in turn feel defensive and backed into a corner. A care team member may then overcompensate, trying too hard to have everything be perfect. But we know what can happen then. Even more mistakes get made because they feel nervous or intimidated by a Jalapeno family member. Or they may feel so frustrated by trying to do a good job, yet are being criticized, that you may experience the silent treatment, passive aggressive eye rolling, or a response that you find inappropriate.

I get it! I've had my Jalapeno moments as a family member too. Things happen that can be frustrating, disappointing, or plain wrong. It's not a perfect system, by any means. But remember, the large majority of homes and their care team members are doing their best in challenging circumstances. They want to get it right every time.

It's also important to maintain mutual respect with each other. Perhaps you've noticed more businesses are putting up signs in their workplaces reminding clients to maintain a professional, courteous attitude and support their culture of mutual respect. This reminder applies to everyone.

If you find yourself having more Jalapeno moments than you'd like, ask to speak with one of the managers at the home, such as the Administrator or Director of Care. Share your concerns with the intention of better understanding the issue and from the desire to work together to resolve situations respectfully. If that doesn't create the outcome you desire, then by all means escalate your concerns through the appropriate channels which are typically posted within the home, on their website, or you can reach out to the governing body in your province to seek guidance for complaint resolution.

Based on my experience as a family member, it's likely you'll identify yourself in all three categories at one time or another while you are part of the LTC community. The family flavours provide you with a framework to reflect on as you continue to grow and get more comfortable in your new role.

CHAPTER 15

Common Misconceptions

I n speaking with families, I have learned there are a lot of misconceptions about what the LTC experience will be like. With misconceptions come disappointment when those expectations aren't met. However, it's not the fault of the families that they don't know. It can also be difficult for the home to educate new families on "everything," so I thought it would be helpful to share some common misconceptions and provide helpful information. I encourage you to make note of any that you'd like to better understand, and connect with a management team member to discuss.

1. I thought my loved one was going to get 24/7 one-on-one care.

An LTC facility runs 24/7, with three shifts of employees covering days, evenings, and nights. There is 24/7 care, however, it's not one-on-one. The average home in Canada can have between 100 to 150 residents. There are of course smaller and larger homes. The typical employee to resident ratio is one-to-one – meaning if you have 100 residents living in a home, you typically will have 100 employees. However, those employees include people who work in the kitchen, dining room, attend to laundry, housekeeping, maintenance, as well as management and clerical staff, in addition to care staff roles such as Registered Nurses, Registered Practical Nurses and Personal Support Workers.

I think this misconception comes from reading information that refers to 24/7 and an assumption is quickly made that their loved one will be cared for one-on-one.

There is no set timeframe as to the total number of hours a resident will receive direct one-on-one care. It depends on each resident's individualized care plan. However, as you can imagine, in a home with many residents requiring different levels of care, it will vary.

2. I thought clothing wouldn't get lost or damaged – after all, they're labelled!

LTC homes have large laundry facilities. It's an incredible amount of washing, folding, and distributing clothing to all of the 100 plus residents. I know I lose socks and I live on my own! This tends to be one of the most common complaints families have, and it's just not possible for the home to always get it right

I recall walking down the hall of my mom's home to visit her. I saw a woman wheeling herself to her room and I recognized she was wearing my mom's sweater. Now I wasn't about to go up and tell her that wasn't her sweater and she needed to give it back. I did let management know, although I'm not sure my description of "an elderly grey-haired woman in a wheelchair" was quite enough.

With bulk washing in industrial machines, then the sorting (can you imagine how many pairs of socks are washed on a weekly basis?) and redistribution, it's important to keep in mind that this is a massive and complex process that won't be right 100% of the time.

I would recommend if there are pieces of clothing that are delicate or have sentimental value, you launder them yourself, or not bring these items to the home. Unfortunately, it's one of the realities of communal living.

3. I should always be able to call and speak to a care team member right away.

Wouldn't it be great if you didn't have to leave a voicemail, particularly if you're feeling anxious and wondering if your loved one had lunch today, or was able to have their bath without any issues? Perhaps you've sent an email outlining your concerns and are waiting for an immediate response.

Much of the work done is "on the floor" with residents. For example, Registered staff have a schedule for dispensing medications to the residents. It can create a serious safety issue if a care team member is interrupted while administering medications. This is particularly important when Registered staff are at their med cart preparing medications for residents.

In addition, there are peak times based on care schedules, meals, and activities when it's harder to connect with a care team member.

If the care team are sitting at the nurse's station, they're typically making notes in a resident's chart or getting caught up on other paperwork. They may already be on the phone with a physician, hospital, or another health provider or family. Don't assume that they're gossiping or taking a break.

4. I thought my loved one would have the same people taking care of them every day.

Having new people providing care can be hard for sure! Your loved one gets used to having the same team members take care of them. The residents and care providers get to know each other, their personalities and create a connection. It's nice to have that consistency.

However, the reality of our working world is there's turnover (and LTC is no different). People decide to leave to work elsewhere, retire, or are let go. As new people are hired, they need to be onboarded and trained and learn each resident's care plan and preferences.

Some care homes have what's called a "primary care model" where a resident is assigned to specific staff (their primary care providers) and their replacement, if team members are sick or on vacation. With this model, there's more consistency between care provider and resident. However, the model is impacted when staff leave their employment and need to be replaced.

Care providers may move within the home for a variety of reasons. Sometimes they request a transfer to another floor because of conflict or friction with a family member. Or there's an accommodation that needs to be made based on a team member's health.

All that is to say: it's challenging to provide the same care staff for three shifts. There will be new people you'll meet and they'll experience that initial learning curve when it comes to the care and routine of your loved one.

Take the time to meet and get to know any new team members. Be patient and try to appreciate they are doing their best in a busy and active environment.

5. If there is a care plan, then everything on that care plan should be done every day.

In an ideal world, that would be true. Unfortunately, not every day is ideal. It may be a day on the care plan where your loved one is normally scheduled for a bath. Yet when the time comes, they refuse to have a bath, and they have that right. The staff will try various strategies to follow the care plan, often with success. However, there will be times where it infringes on a resident's rights.

There may also be times when a shave or brushing hair isn't done at the time the care plan states. It may be because another part of the care plan took much longer, and the team member has run out of time. Or there may have been an emergency. Before jumping to conclusions, just ask.

6. The only way to get respect and resolve a problem is to be the squeaky wheel and escalate it to the highest level.

I can see how families may believe this, particularly as long term care homes are overseen by government regulations and requirements. But it's not the only way to seek resolution. Each home has a management team that typically reports to a Regional Manager or Director, then perhaps to a Vice President in the corporate office. I recommend starting with the person you want clarification from or seek to resolve an issue with. If this doesn't provide the solution you want, then go to the next level of management. Good homes want to resolve issues as quickly and effectively as possible and work with the family in good faith.

I understand how frustrating it can be if you're feeling like your loved one isn't getting the care they need. If it seems the staff don't care, or you're not getting answers to questions quickly enough, it will help to adopt an attitude of curiosity and maintain a calm demeanor.

When we have a gap in the information we seek, or in how we feel we're being treated, we can get triggered very quickly and react in a passionate or impulsive way. Unfortunately, and on too many occasions, homes have had to endure poorly behaved family members. Staff have been subjected to yelling and swearing. There have been times in the heat of the moment where family members have voiced degrading and derogatory comments to staff members. This behaviour is, without exception, completely unacceptable. Imagine how hurtful and demoralizing this is for the caregivers. And the damage inflicted to the family/staff/resident relationship is beyond measure.

From my personal experience as a family member and hearing other family members' stories, this level of frustration is fueled by emotion and reactivity. It's then less likely we can approach the situation with a reasonable and responsive mindset. That's why it's important to focus on a collaborative solution versus spiraling into a reactive, defensive state.

If family complaining is ongoing and intense, staff have been known to avoid making eye contact, or even avoid you altogether. In my workshops I ask staff if they duck into a resident's room to hide when they see a challenging family come down the hall. Or if they bend down to tie their shoelaces, even though their shoes don't have any? And the answer is YES! Most care team members nod with a knowing look of "Yup, we've totally done that."

The rush to escalate a situation can also create a breach of trust and respect between yourself and the care providers, which is essential in continuing to work together as partners in care.

7. If I complain, the staff will take it out on my loved one.

It's so interesting when I share this family concern with care team members. They look at me like I have three heads! Staff build relationships with their residents based on each person's needs, interests, conversations, and care. Team members grow to really love and adore their residents. After all, they are helping your loved one with their personal care, as well as their emotional care. It's always a welcomed situation when the family is pleasant to deal with and appreciative of the work the staff do.

When families have a concern and can voice it appropriately and respectfully, it helps provide useful feedback for staff to better understand if there's a care gap, or an information or expectation gap. It invites conversation to take place, so staff and families can work together to resolve the issue and enable the highest level of care.

Typically, care team members don't view the actions or behaviours of a family as a reflection of the resident. There are two distinct types of relationships. One is with the residents they directly care for, the other is with the family as partners in care.

I don't hear team members complaining about their residents and the level of care they require. More often, I hear about the frustration they feel with the families. While this concern is valid, it's more likely that care team members will avoid interacting with challenging families but still continue to love and care for their residents.

8. Now that they're in long term care, my loved one is going to improve or get better. (Otherwise known as "I expect the staff to work miracles.")

Sometimes this does happen. For example, if a resident wasn't able to get exercise or social stimulation before and is experiencing that now, it can definitely improve their physical and/or emotional state.

More often than not though, a resident has been approved for LTC because their condition requires care that is unmanageable or unsustainable for a family member, hospital, or retirement home to provide.

At times, we wish a more clinical level of care will help our loved one improve their ability to walk, communicate, or engage. And sometimes that does happen, particularly if the resident was more isolated prior to coming into a care home. However, there are times that it won't happen and expecting your loved one to improve isn't a reasonable expectation, no matter how much you wish it was.

Care team members working in LTC have pretty well seen it all. They can recognize the signs and symptoms and know the typical trajectory of most diseases. Understandably, families have a difficult time believing or accepting this reality. This can cause frustration when an improvement to their loved one's condition doesn't occur. And that frustration can turn into finger pointing and blaming, primarily driven by wishful thinking.

9. **Staff should know where my loved one is when I call or visit.**

Your loved one may be less dependent on support and able to get around independently by walking or in a wheelchair. If residents go for a walk or participate in a social activity, care team members may not know where they are at that particular moment. Remember, this is now your loved one's home and they have the freedom to explore, visit another resident, attend an activity or social function. It can be worrisome for families to arrive at the home and fully expect their loved one to be sitting in their room or participating in a specific activity. When this happens to you, take a deep breath and check in with one of the care team members. In addition, getting to know your loved one's routine and preferences will help you locate them more easily by yourself.

10. I thought I'd feel more settled and relieved now that my loved one is in long term care, or I thought the adjustment would take longer.

It's hard to know what you will feel and experience during this transition. It may be the first and only time you admit a loved one into a care home. Some families find it an immediate relief, particularly if they've been white knuckling it at home and have felt the strain of physically and emotionally caring for an ailing parent or spouse. Alternatively, a loved one may have transitioned from hospital or a retirement home to LTC, so you've already made the first big leap into a more institutional setting. What tends to happen is residents adjust to their new surroundings first, then the care team members adjust to caring for their new resident. Often, it's the families who have the longest period of adjustment. There are many conflicting emotions at play here. You're adjusting to your life without your loved one at home, as well as unfamiliar staff, new routines and schedules. It's important to acknowledge what you're feeling and look for support if you're struggling to accept or adjust to these changes. Refer back to the chapters that outline the Seven A's. Use the questions at the end of each chapter for reflection and discussion with your family or other people in your support system, including team members in your loved one's home.

11. I should be able to get a parking spot when I come to visit.

Yes, it can be very frustrating when there's only so much time to visit and there's zero parking. It may seem like every family is visiting at the same time as you. This is an issue that's unlikely to be resolved due to limited space. If this becomes a regular occurrence, ask the home to let you know what their parking situation is like and the less busy times, so you can plan your visit accordingly.

12. I thought I'd get regular detailed updates about my loved one's activities, participation, medical information, eating habits, etc.

You'd be amazed at what gets "charted" by the staff in your loved one's file. Not only how much food and drink they've consumed, but how much they've eliminated too – yes, bowel movements and urination are also tracked. Staff track any activities residents participate in, as well as the administration of their medication. While a lot gets documented, it's not always possible to tell you everything that your loved one has been up to in a single day. When there are significant changes or events that happen, a care team member will reach out with a call to let you know. But if a loved one was finicky at dinner and just didn't feel like eating, that's typically not going to warrant a mention – unless it becomes a pattern or a red flag.

The transition from providing care and knowing every little nuance about your loved one to becoming a visitor can feel strange. However, asking care team members a million questions about your loved one's daily routine takes them away from providing care to your family member and other residents. It's better to figure out what updates are important for you to know, and why.

13. I thought our care conference would be more comprehensive with information updates and be easier to get scheduled.

How I wish it wasn't called a care conference. It sounds like a big important meeting. Yet what it really is, is a way to set a baseline for your loved one's care and to check in on what's important.

The first care conference is scheduled about four to six weeks after admission day, depending on the physician's schedule and availability. This is "setting the baseline." What that means is, staff have had time to better understand your loved one's health issues, their medications, and overall disposition. By now, your loved one has had a few weeks to adjust to their new home. The care team members are learning about your loved one's particular habits and care needs. The file that was created at the time of admission is reviewed by a doctor. The medication is reviewed with the family, and any recommended changes are discussed

Typically, a doctor is present for 10 to 15 minutes to review all the above. The rest of the care conference involves an overview of other areas such as your family member's diet and eating habits, any activities they've shown interest in, as well as their overall engagement in their new home setting. It's also an opportunity for you to ask questions and build a relationship with the team who are caring for your loved one.

After the initial care conference, follow up conferences are scheduled annually. However, you can always request a meeting or conversation between care conferences to address specific concerns. As well, there are quarterly summary notes that become part of the resident's health care record. If you are a POA (Power of Attorney) or Substitute Decision Maker, you can also request to see their health record if you have a specific concern you'd like to review.

14. I thought it would be easier to connect with other family members at the home.

Some families want to build relationships with other families who are also visiting loved ones. I recall when my husband first became a resident, I wanted to connect with his roommate's wife. Our husbands were similar ages ("younger" residents, compared to the majority)and I was looking to connect with someone who "knows the ropes." However, she worked shifts and I was working in my corporate job. It just didn't happen.

If this is important to you, speak with the Administrator or other care team members and let them know you'd appreciate some introductions. Another approach is to just introduce yourself to families that you see at the home and let them know you would love the opportunity to have a conversation. Every family was once a new family. On the flip side, if you see a new family member struggling or looking lost, reach out and offer some friendly help.

Homes also have Family Councils. A Family Council is comprised of family members within the home community who work with the LTC team to identify and resolve issues that affect residents' quality of life. They also plan activities for residents, families, and staff, and are there to support each other. You may want to inquire about your home's Family Council and connect with their members.

15. I thought the staff would be more proactive in alerting me to any additional issues – for example, foot care, or changes to their habits or behaviours.

As family members, we can sometimes think, assume, or expect that the staff will notice every little thing about our loved one. I remember wishing that was true as well. My mom's toenails were—well, let's just say they needed some work.

In LTC, care team members don't directly deal with advanced foot care (i.e. complex situations like diabetes, or circulatory issues that would require a podiatrist or nurse), but you can arrange for a third party to come in. You can ask them if they can arrange a podiatry service for a fee, or bring a preferred provider in. I was likely given the information on admission day, but with so much coming at me, I just didn't remember.

If there are changes in behaviour or habits that are pronounced or are significant, then this typically will prompt a conversation to bring it to your attention. It's the slight changes that can go unnoticed by staff but would be more obvious to you.

16. I thought their room would be secure.

Due to safety issues, individual room doors in LTC can't be locked. So yes, it's possible that many people are coming and going into your loved ones' room multiple times a day. It's also possible that other residents may wander into the room – perhaps from confusion or curiosity.

From a staffing perspective, care team members come in to help with personal care. Housekeeping comes in to clean and tidy. There are laundry staff who collect soiled clothing and deliver laundered items. There are also Registered staff who dispense medication. In addition, there are times that your loved one isn't in their room, leaving it unattended as they go for meals or activities.

If your loved one is in a semi-private room, then they're sharing space (and a bathroom) with a roommate. This may also impact the number of people coming into their room.

LTC homes are a community setting where individual rooms and residents' belongings are not always secure. Although there are rarely any incidents, it's always recommended that valuables are not brought into the home.

17.   I thought we would have more than just 24 hours to clean the room out after our loved one passes away.

Likely during the admission process, you were advised that when the time comes and your loved one passes away, there is a 24-hour timeframe to clean the room by removing all personal belongings. Most families don't remember this, which is completely understandable. There's so much to take in, and most are certainly not thinking about their loved one dying during the admission experience.

What can happen though, when their loved one does pass, is that the family gets really upset about being 'pushed' to clean everything out. It's even harder if there are lots of clothing, furniture and personal belongings that need to be packed up. Or the family lives out of town and needs to coordinate all of the necessary steps with funeral planning and arrangements.

This is not a conversation that the staff look forward to by any means. They are also grieving the loss of your loved one – their resident that they have grown quite close to. And they also know that within about 72 hours, there will be a new resident moving into that room.

I've heard families and staff criticize this as being callous, or 'profit driven' when actually, this is a process mandated by the governing body if the home is publicly funded. In many locations, there is a lengthy waiting list. Perhaps you were on the waiting list before you got the call. And the previous resident needed to vacate that bed in order for it to be available for you.

Although you likely don't want to think about when the day comes, it is helpful to keep in mind that this transactional part of the process, with cleaning out the room in a timely way, is necessary. And with that you are helping the next family who may be desperately waiting for the call to say their loved one has been accepted for placement in their care home.

18. If I'm the POA (Power of Attorney) for health, then I should be able to make all the decisions on behalf of my loved one.

Let me start by saying that I am not offering any legal advice on this topic. Each province has full information regarding POA that you can easily access online. Alternatively, speak with your lawyer regarding any legal interpretation questions, and your loved one's physician for questions related to care. Also, the Administrators and Directors of Care will be well-versed in this complex topic. All that to say, it's important that you understand the type of POA you have (financial and/or health) and your role, responsibilities, as well as the scope of your decision-making ability.

The POA for health (it can also be called a Medical POA, Healthy Proxy or Health Care Directive) deals with decisions about care. For example, it doesn't give the POA power about friendships or visitors. This can come up if the family wants to prevent certain visitors or friendships. If the resident wishes and welcomes those visitors, the LTC home cannot prevent them visiting or interfere with privacy. (I recommend you ask for a copy of the Residents' Bill of Rights from the long term care legislation as a reference).

When your loved one designates you as their POA for health they are expressing in writing their health care wishes for when they're no longer able to personally communicate those themself.

It gives the designated person the ability to make decisions about their health care if they become mentally incapable of making health-related decisions.

And that's the key part – if they are deemed to be mentally incapable. Some families can get quite frustrated with care providers when they want to make a decision on behalf of their loved one, but their loved one is still competent. The POA has no power as the attorney (in this case, attorney doesn't mean a lawyer, it means a trusted representative for the giver) as long as a resident is competent and mentally capable to make their own decisions.

As POA your responsibility is to make decisions that your loved one would have made if they were competent. In other words, you need to think about what the person would want, not necessarily whether you as the POA would agree with it.

I can't stress enough the importance of having a clear understanding of this, appreciating the responsibilities involved, as well as the limitations of being your loved one's POA.

19. I didn't think residents in LTC would (or should) be sexually active.

Even I'M squirming as I write this. I mean, we don't like to think of our parents as sexual beings at the best of times! Or if it's your spouse who is a resident, how does this impact your ability to be intimate with each other? Perhaps your spouse has dementia and doesn't know who you are any more, and they've made a new friend in the home? Or maybe you haven't given this any thought, and now it's something else to think and worry about.

This can be an uncomfortable conversation for many reasons. And this is something that long term care homes deal with and support their residents and families with more than you can imagine. But they can feel uncomfortable bringing it up, without knowing if this is something you want to better understand.

If this is something you want to learn more about, I suggest you ask the Administrator or the Director of Care for a meeting so that you can let them know you want to better understand what the options are and how this could work.

20. My loved one should be getting more care than they're getting, given how much we're paying.

Let me start by saying that LTC is a complex and highly regulated part of the health care system in Canada. There are entire books and journals written about this, so I'm not even going to attempt to get into detail. But it's worth addressing here, because as a customer – a family member – it's helpful to understand the basics.

In Canada, LTC is provided by for-profit, not-for-profit, and municipal homes. The consistency with all three is that they are all publicly funded and regulated.

The hours of care and reimbursement structure is determined by the government. However, government doesn't fund LTC 100%. There is a portion that is paid by the resident (or family) which is calculated and confirmed upon admission. That amount is paid monthly.

The level of acuity with residents is much higher now than it was when homes were first established. That is before my time, but it wasn't uncommon to have residents who had cars and still drove themselves. Their health conditions were much less complex and required less care.

There may be times where you feel that the home isn't providing the level of care you would like to see. And yet, with the legislation and regulations, the homes have limitations on staffing levels and ability to do any more than what's legislatively mandated.

If you want a higher level of support, you can supplement with additional care. Some families hire private care providers to provide companionship and basic support for their loved one at their home.

No system is perfect and you may experience some frustration with unmet expectations. There are many moving parts in LTC and I truly believe that the care team and management strive to do their best with the resources they have.

CHAPTER 16

Dancing with the Grief

I have mentioned in this book how therapy was one of the strategies for self-care I embraced when my husband went into care. For me, it was a safe place to share and process how I was feeling. Therapy was also a way to learn practical strategies to help support myself. And that in turn allowed me to better support my family.

I met Edy Nathan through a course we took together and there we had many conversations about grief. After all, this is her area of expertise, both personally and professionally.

I asked Edy to share some of her expertise in this book, so that you can learn a bit more about the grief journey and how it may show up for you during this time.

I had never heard of terms like "complicated grief" or "anticipatory grief" before reading Edy's work. And yet, that was something my kids *and I, as well as Ty's family, were experiencing. Understanding grief and accepting its presence helped us on our journey.*

I hope that Edy's words provide some insight, comfort, and assurance that you're not alone. That you can, in your own way, dance with grief.

....

Now what? The decision is made. The transition of moving your loved one into LTC is something we might try to avoid but now must face. Having no choice in the matter often feels like our hand has been forced, while a thoughtful decision can help create a greater sense of control. For some people, the shock of having to act fast without much thought requires action first, then feeling follows later. When people perform Herculean tasks, like picking up a car in a state of emergency, the emotional shock of such an act hits at a later point.

Even when the professional staff at the home are helpful, friendly, and comforting, you might notice an emotional experience which few may reference after leaving a family member in the care of others. Here's what it is: grief.

Grief is what informs this kind of emotional flooding. It is intense and it is stressful. Grief is like the after effect of an unexpected storm rolling in, not really knowing how hard it will hit, what damage will ensue, or how to pick up the pieces after. Transitioning your loved one into LTC is stressful. Naming grief as part of the stress reaction is not a go-to explanation for the diverse emotions at hand. This type of grief is tricky. It is not grief resulting from the loss of a loved one, but grief over the changes in your life and the life of your family member. You have probably been busy getting everything in place, making the hard decision to make this move. This busyness may have kept you from recognizing the deep emotion of grief, as it silently creeps in. It waits for you to ease up on all the planning, the final decision-making, before making its presence known.

As you navigate through this journey with your loved one, grief is waiting for you. It reveals itself in unknown ways. As hard as this time is, with every loss, you have the opportunity to learn about yourself, what you need, how to create boundaries, and how to protect yourself.

Grief is non-linear. It does not follow any plan nor can its effects be charted in a particular order. That's part of what makes grief hard to navigate, understand, and move through. When you don't know how it's going to show up, it's hard to prepare for how to handle it.

It's hard to admit, not only to yourself but to your family, that you can't care for your loved one any longer. Facing these life-altering, monumental decisions, like when and how to tell your loved one and actually moving them into a care home are elements which lead to a mosaic of grief. Guilt, confusion, anger, and denial are some of the feelings which contribute to the mosaic. Grief affects the mind, the body and for many, their spiritual beliefs. This is what some experts refer to as a spiritual emergency.

I realized this kind of grief took up residence in my own heart when my partner needed to be in a transition program after a cancer diagnosis. At first, I believed I could be his caretaker. It may have been a bit of an ego thing, which is often what's at play when making hard decisions. I was 26-years-old and energy and commitment were not the issues. Yet, his needs were far greater and more intense than I had the ability or knowledge to handle. It was the first time I had to admit that his illness was bigger than both of us. The day I left him at the program, I cried. Intense guilt and anxiety pulsed through me, wreaking emotional havoc. I kept trying to ignore what I felt. Do you know what that did? It made those feelings even bigger. The integration of my loss only began once I identified my feelings as grief. What unfolded was a sharing of the loss of the "us" we used to know. Yet, it also allowed for greater intimacy and tenderness. When we stopped avoiding, we realized how much more we could share in the struggle of this loss and the bandit that was stealing the life we knew.

Here is an outline for six of the most prevalent phases within grief. These phases do not follow any specific order, although the first phase, emotional armour, may be one you visit often. You will learn about fear and anger, emotional armour and even role confusion as part of the myriad of grief responses you may experience.

Though I only discuss six phases here, I delve into 11 phases in greater detail in my book, *It's Grief: The Dance of Self-Discovery through*

Trauma and Loss. The information below will help you to understand and navigate through the primary emotions of grief. Everyone experiences grief differently. You may only relate to one of the phases, or you may resonate with all of them. Give yourself permission to take what you need at this moment. Sometimes an emotion which is not felt or understood at the beginning of a transitional time can surface at a later time. Remember, there isn't a right order to how you may experience these various phases.

THE **SIX** PHASES OF GRIEF

1. EMOTIONAL ARMOUR

We all need a protective armour when facing grief. The first phase I describe is exactly that. It protects you until you are ready to move into the next phases. This is what I like to call the "go back and reset phase." Since it serves as protection, it can be a resting place.

Though it will be different for everyone, emotional armour can be experienced in the following ways:

- Numbness - When access to feeling anything is denied, the limbic system in the brain is in full swing. Numbness is as if a fog has descended upon you, not by choice, rather as a respite from the intense feelings associated with grief. Within this arena, there is a sense of nothingness, with little or no response to external stimuli, while offering distance from your emotions. It is an unconscious place to gather your wits.

- Emotional agitation - Have you ever seen someone moan, yell, cry uncontrollably, or breathe as if they can't catch a breath? This is what emotional agitation looks like and it can be intense. It is a place where the emotions live within the brain. This is the amygdala and the entire limbic system. When emotional overwhelm trumps your ability to think straight, it can feel like a bandit has arrived within your psyche. Bandits don't enter with permission, and emotional overwhelm happens without permission. When the emotions invade you it affects thoughts, clarity, and calm. It is a culmination of the emotions that may have not been expressed prior to moving your loved one into LTC. What's interesting here is how often after an emotional agitation, clarity often follows.

- Denial - This is not happening. It doesn't need to happen. I don't need anyone to help me.

- Protest - I am not going to do this. Leave me alone. I'm not talking about it.

2. ROLE CONFUSION

During this time, you may be asking yourself: Who am I now that my loved one is living in an LTC home? Your roles as caretaker, sibling, child, or spouse have shifted, and you don't know how to navigate your way through this. However, with more time you have the opportunity to explore new roles. You may be wondering: Is that okay?

3. THE THREE D'S

- **Distraction** - Grief is a big distractor. Our concentration is greatly affected, decision making may not be as clear or concise as it once was. Many of us find it hard to get tasks done or accomplished.

- **Depression** - This is different from sadness. Depression robs you of your ability to live life fully. At its worst, it causes issues around sleep, food, relationships, and work. Depression shows up as an absence of caring about anything, as if in a fog. It affects your thoughts, desire to interact with others, and stirs a deep sense of pessimism.

- **Detachment** – Indifference and disinterest are aspects of detachment. Though your thoughts may be foggy, you're still going about your day: sleeping, eating, going to work. Detachment is different than numbness, as it is often based on a choice you've made. It's actually a good behavior or emotion to choose, especially if facing a sense of deep overwhelm or are in a state of being overloaded with information. The multiple tasks needing to be accomplished are part of the entire process of getting your loved one into an LTC facility. It can serve as a break from demands made on you, while allowing for a bit of a respite from the emotional roller coaster. However, while detachment gives you time to just be, it can also mask what's really going on in your life. When detached, you avoid joy, fun, or interpersonal interactions. Detachment can happen when you are filled with hidden, unexpressed emotions. The detachment can last for hours or days. If you find its lasting longer than that, you might consider speaking to a professional.

4. FEAR AND ANXIETY

These two emotions often go hand in hand. Anxiety surfaces alongside fear. Fear arises because of something that's happened in the past, while anxiety shows up when thinking about what is to come. Neither one feels good. Heart racing, thoughts that won't quiet, or become obsessive. If you find this to be true for you, stay with the facts or data of what is actually occurring.

5. ANGER, RAGE, AND DESPAIR.

Anger is often used to fight for what you believe in. It can overtake you or it can inform you about how deeply you care. Responding with anger to a situation where you would normally be cool or collected is another aspect of how grief expresses itself. Anger can be internalized or externalized and is often felt when things aren't going according to plan or are out of your control. It is summoned when you need to fight for what you believe in. It can move from an internalized place within you to an externalized place. When unexpressed, it is an internal experience, seeming as if you are stuck in a debilitating silence, holding the depth of this raw emotion within you. When you acknowledge its presence, which is a first step in dealing with this potent emotion, it has less of a chance to overtake you. In this form, you get to know your anger as an ally, letting you in on how deeply you care. Anger, especially when it shows up unannounced, meaning you were not planning on having an angry outburst, can come out sideways, leaving you feeling unheard or unseen. When this occurs, it is the antithesis of what may have motivated you to get angry in the first place: to be heard, understood or seen. In this case, it is often filled with a sense of feeling awkward, especially when the anger quickly and uncontrollably bubbles up inside of you, and the ability to control your impulse to yell is non-existent.

Rage, a deeper more aggressive form of anger, often occurs when anger has been held in and not expressed or even acknowledged by you, for far too long. The rage rampage can also be internalized or externalized. Filled with a fury not yet expressed, the internal rage might cause you to self-harm (excessive behaviors) or harm others (verbally act out). It's more than displeasure, it is wrath and indignation for what you see or hear or feel. Externalized, rage rarely gets the right kind of attention. It's passionate plea often happens when you have to come to an end point. Some of the emotional circumstances around this end point are an extreme sense of isolation and aloneness while on your journey with a loved one.

With both anger and rage, if you acknowledge their presence, you have really taken a first step to quieting their forces. Sometimes when the unexpressed gets expressed it can seem as if some superpower within you has just shown up. You can also temper rage and anger by also tracking what you feel.

Write down what you feel or sense about the situation you're in. Asking yourself: Am I angry? Have I shared this anger with anyone other than myself? Do I understand why I'm angry? Also write down three ways you know you express anger, such as: 1. Silence. 2. Eating 3. Sharing. Do these strategies work for you? Does your anger seem resolved when you cope with it in your usual ways?

Why write? Because you are taking the feelings within and shifting them outside of you. We know that the limbic system which holds a lot of emotions and responses to emotions, gets relief when you write things down or discuss what's going on within you. This is one way to track the emotions of anger and rage. You also become acquainted with any anger you're experiencing. The rage will be quieted if you become aware of the anger before it becomes more powerful and transitions into rage.

Despair is related to a sense of hopelessness. Filled with palpable pain, the dejection which occurs when in a place of despair is certainly displacing. You might find yourself meeting a loss of hope, not due to anything that you've done or are thinking about doing, rather because you may not have the ability to control an outcome, like the aging process or an illness.

6. Regret, guilt, and shame

Author Lewis Smedes defines guilt and shame with simplicity and clarity: *"The difference between guilt and shame is very clear—in theory. We feel guilty for what we do. We feel shame for what we are."* Deciding to transition a family member into an LTC home causes a multitude of emotions. Guilt and shame are often the most prevalent. The grief from guilt comes in many forms. Internal conversations such as: "I should've done things differently for my loved one"; or "I should've seen the signs of their aging or dementia sooner, so I could've gotten them help before they needed this kind of care." These are statements of guilt and regret. The shame element arises out of past conversations with our loved one and the promises made to them which we can no longer honour.

With each of these six phases, think about where you are on the spectrum of these emotional experiences as you face this transition.

Like grief, the process of bringing your loved one into a long term care home is not linear. Expectations get in the way of our growth. Looking at grief as a fluid process can help you to be fluid in processing this enormous shift in your life.

As I end many of my writings: You've got this. You've had the power all along. When you're ready, you can do what you need to do.

Edy Nathan MA, LCSWR is a licensed therapist with more than 20 years experience. She has degrees from New York University and Fordham University, with post-graduate training at the Ackerman Institute for Family Therapy. She practices in New York City. Edy is the author of It's *Grief: The Dance of Self-Discovery through Trauma and Loss.*

CHAPTER 17

Final Thoughts

A s you begin your journey as a family member in long term care, I hope you found the information in this book helpful. My goal is to provide you with some practical tools and insights to help you manage the emotional journey as a family member.

The time you spend in this community may be days, weeks, months, or years. It could be a place you visit regularly or sporadically. If you live a distance away, you may have to rely on the phone or video conferencing to connect with your loved one and care team members.

You have joined a club that perhaps you never anticipated being a member of. And yet here you are, with the rest of us, learning as you go.

When Ty became a resident, I couldn't possibly know he would live in the home for four years. At the time, his specialist deemed him palliative. We were told ECD was incurable, degenerative, and fatal. Medical practitioners thought Ty would be lucky to survive another year, possibly two.

Knowing that each day was probably going to be the best he was going to feel, and that his physical and cognitive abilities would continue to decline, I myself needed to work through each of the Seven A's shared in this book. But I couldn't have done it on my own. Building a support team, both formal and informal, was a lifeline for me and my kids.

I had a therapist who helped me work through my emotions as well as the logistics of my new role as a resident's spouse. I counted on her to help me maintain a healthy perspective in an extremely challenging time. I also had friends who would check in with me, who would be there to listen, or to have a conversation that wasn't only about Ty's illness.

It was important for me to plan things to look forward to, whether it was going to the movies, or lunch with a girlfriend, or an overnight getaway while I had a family member keep an eye on the kids. Small manageable activities that got me out of my day to day routine without having to plan and prepare too much. I wasn't perfect at this by any means, but I did find this helpful for my mental health.

As I shared earlier, it's important to be able to accept this new reality. Although that doesn't mean you have to like what's happening. I remember my therapist asking me, "After Ty is gone and you look back at this time, how do you want to remember it?" She asked me to consider how I wanted to feel. How did I want my kids to feel?

As hard as it was to think about that, I really appreciated her questions. It gave me permission to lean into this experience. Whether I wanted to or not didn't matter – this was our reality. I realized I could choose to be angry, upset, sad, kicking and fighting all the way. Or I could release all of that, accept what is, and make the best of it.

I used her questions as guideposts to navigate what I was experiencing. I wanted to live with as little regret as possible. I wanted to be there for Ty with compassion and presence. I wanted to notice the little moments that mattered with him and his care team. I wanted to remember the tears of sadness as well as the tears of gratitude. I wanted to remember the hugs from the care team and leave them with a positive impression, as they had with me. And I wanted to remember how I played a positive role – to the best of my ability – as a member of their community.

I didn't get it right every time. But I did recognize that I had the ability to choose how I was going to respond to whatever was happening. The times I was able to do that didn't mean the sadness or tears went away. What it did do was open up my ability to experience the happy moments, the funny moments, the heartfelt moments, even the frustrating moments and challenging moments. To remember the moments that mattered.

Moments like helping Ty drink his thickened juice through a straw that I needed to hold for him. Or feeding him his pureed dinner because he was at risk of choking. I could view it as a task, or I could view it as a privilege.

I would sit with him while he watched TV then dozed off. For a moment I could pretend it was just like our usual Friday night. Or telling him he needed to turn the TV down in the community room, because he was watching a mob movie with lots of violence and swearing, and the other residents weren't having it! I could see the humour in Ty, as a younger resident, creating a bit of a ruckus.

Another time, staff told me that Ty has to stop hiding fruit in different drawers in the building because it'll attract ants. He was being crafty and resourceful! Or seeing Ty wearing someone else's shirt because the laundry got mixed up and he LOVED his new shirt. He was grateful to be the recipient of this mistake.

Then there were the phone calls from team members telling me that Ty had "eloped" again (this is what care workers call it when a resident is 'exit seeking' and escapes from the home!) to wheel himself down to the local pub for a beer. I wish I'd cut him more slack about those escapades...

How you choose to react or respond to this new reality is a choice. With all of our relationships, the choice is always yours.

Let me leave you with these last brief thoughts:

Make moments matter.

Look for what's working.

Practice self-care.

Be present.

Be grateful.

Be patient.

Be kind.

With yourself, with your loved one, and with all the people who you count on to care.

ACKNOWLEDGEMENTS

I have had the privilege to work and connect with thousands of care team members from the front line to the executive level in Seniors' Care. I am incredibly grateful for the trust they've given to me to share my stories and frameworks to help them build strong, healthy relationships with their residents' families. Thank you for inviting me into your homes and creating the space for the powerful conversations and connections with your teams, residents and families. It was through these conversations that this book became a reality.

Transforming an idea onto the page and writing a book so that it can be a helpful resource for families and care providers takes a team approach. I am immensely grateful for my friends, colleagues and residents' families who were my advance readers and shared their feedback and insights. I'm so glad you are part of this journey.

To my friend Liz Long, who is also in the "resident's family member club," thank you for the many hours of conversation, brainstorming, tears and laughter. You have always supported the work I do with your curiosity, encouragement and humour. I am so grateful for our friendship.

To my friend Mary Osborne, who read more than a few manuscript versions with a great eye for detail. Thank you for your incredible positivity and enthusiasm. As our Maid of Honour way back in 1986 you have been on this road with us and I appreciate you.

I am grateful for my new-found friendship with Barbara Tarrant, who generously wrote the foreword. You are walking the family member's journey with grit and grace, while continuing to be a leader in your husband's home.

I'm also grateful for Edy Nathan's friendship and contribution to this book, and the courageous work she does with grief education and support. Thank you for caring so much for people, and your ongoing commitment to help us dance with the grief.

Thank you to my amazing editor Amanda Lee, who not only helped with structure, she challenged me to dig deeper with my personal experiences and reflections. Thank you for not tiring of my constant questions, and bad jokes.

To my children Taylor and Logan who lived through the heartbreaking and unimaginable experience of losing their dad. I am so proud of your courage, compassion and how you have traveled this emotional journey while growing into incredibly kind human beings. I love you both so very much.

And finally, to Charlie – my cat who thinks he's a dog. Thank you for being my writing companion and knowing how to best distract me with your irresistible attention seeking ways.

Additional Resources

Here is a list of books that helped me through my journey, or ones I have read since:

The Power of TED* (*The Empowerment Dynamic) by David Emerald

Man's Search for Meaning by Viktor Frankl

If I Understood You, Would I Have This Look on My Face? By Alan Alda

It's Grief: The Dance of Self-Discovery Through Trauma and Loss by Edy Nathan

Broken Open: How Difficult Times Can Help Us Grow by Elizabeth Lesser

The Big Leap: Conquer Your Hidden Fear and Take Life to the Next Level by Gay Hendricks

When Things Fall Apart: Heart Advice for Difficult Times by Pema Chödrön

When The Body Says No: The Cost of Hidden Stress by Gabor Maté M.D.

The Untethered Soul: The Journey Beyond Yourself by Michael A. Singer

About the Author

Deborah Bakti is the author of RECIPE for Empathy: Six Strategies to Transform your family into Fans in Seniors' Care. Deborah is the owner of THINK Breakthrough Inc., where she delivers workplace coaching, training, and consulting to the seniors' care sector. Prior to that, Deborah worked in leadership roles in various sectors and spent the last decade in health care.

Deborah is the proud mom of Taylor and Logan. She lives in Burlington, Ontario with her cat, Charlie.